THE QUIZ-AND-ANSWER BOOK

The
QUIZ-AND-ANSWER
BOOK

2222 New Questions Asked
2222 Authentic Answers

by

FREDERIC J. HASKIN
"The Answers-to-Questions Man"

GROSSET & DUNLAP
Publishers   New York

Printed in the United States of America

FOREWORD

The Quiz is America's current pastime, so the purpose of this book is primarily entertainment. In it you will find 2222 questions and answers, which cover such a broad field as to be of interest to everyone.

To those who have avocations or hobbies the subject questionnaires should have a special appeal, and give them a chance to mark up a high score.

The majority of the questions are new and have not appeared in the Answers to Questions Books heretofore published. They are widely varied and designed for the general reader.

The Super Quizzes and the Brain Teaser, on the other hand, are frankly "nutcrackers," but, although the questions are sometimes tricky, they should not be outside the scope of the well-informed person.

HOW TO USE THIS BOOK

The competitive spirit is strong in human nature and most of us like to know whether we are any better or any worse than our neighbors. For this reason it is customary to keep score.

Each quiz consists of 25 questions, and by allowing 4 points for each one correctly answered, it is easy to arrive at a percentage. Sixty per cent is considered a good average for the miscellaneous quizzes, but a specialist may score considerably higher in the subjects in which he is particularly interested.

If more miscellaneous quizzes are desired than appear in the book, they can easily be prepared by making typewritten lists of questions culled from the subject chapters.

When the questions are asked orally, it is also possible to use the quizzes backwards, that is, to make the answer the basis for the question, and the question, the answer. For instance, in the Art Quiz, we find the question, "What is a scarab?" Answer: "A stone carved in the form of a beetle." The question may, therefore, be asked, "What is the name for a stone carved in the form of a beetle?" Answer: "A scarab." In this way the use of the book may be varied.

*   *   *   *   *   *   *   *

CONTENTS

CONTENTS

THE QUIZ-AND-ANSWER BOOK

ERRATA SLIP

Page 62, Question 23. Substitute BIRNBAUM for *Birbaum*.

Page 83, Question 9. Substitute EASTER for *Eastern*.

Page 100, Question 25. Substitute GAUDEAMUS for *Guadeamus*.

Page 184, Right hand column, Answer 11. Substitute VICENTE for *Vincente*.

Page 187, Right hand column, Answer 3. Substitute TWELVE for *eleven*.

Page 192, Right hand column, Answer 7. Substitute SULU for *Sula*.

Page 194, Right hand column, Answer 12. The answer should be PYTHAGORAS.

Page 203, Right hand column, Answer 8. Substitute AUGUSTE for *Augusti*.

Page 205, Left hand column, Answer 22. In third line of answer, substitute SWITHIN'S for *Suretin's*.

Page 217, Right hand column, Answer 21. Substitute NO for *Seldom*.

Page 220, Left hand column, Answer 13. In second line of answer, substitute SEA ANIMAL for *fish*.

Page 224, Left hand column, Answer 19. In second line of answer, substitute BELLEEK for *Belleck*.

Page 228, Right hand column, Answer 22. In second line of answer, substitute HAZARDOUS for *portendous*.

Page 229, Right hand column, Answer 8. Substitute TURNAGAIN for *Turngain*.

ART QUIZ NUMBER 1

Your hair may not turn red, but your face will take on a Titian hue (see question 14), before you have answered these twenty-five questions. (You'll find the correct answers on page 179.)

1. Who was known as the faultless painter?
2. What famous Madonna is in the Dresden Gallery?
3. Picasso was the founder of what type of art?
4. Name the artist who sued Ruskin for libel?
5. Who painted the "Age of Innocence?"
6. On which of his works did Rodin spend twenty years?
7. What famous painting was stolen from the Louvre in 1911?
8. Name the painting designed for a dissecting room.
9. In ancient paintings why are some saints shown with a square nimbus?
10. Who designed the Diana atop the old Madison Square Garden?
11. What does the Bayeux tapestry depict?
12. Is the original "Last Supper" by da Vinci still in existence?

13. Who was Praxiteles?
14. What noted artist gave his name to a certain color of hair?
15. Define "pinxit."
16. Name the French artist who took his subjects from the lives of French peasants.
17. In what forms of art did Benvenuto Cellini specialize?
18. Name a famous woman painter of animals.
19. What German artist was a pioneer in the field of engraving?
20. What two great artists did not sign their pictures and why?
21. To what does "still life" painting refer?
22. With what is the name Gobelin connected?
23. What is a rose window?
24. Where is the famous statue depicting the end of the trail?
25. Why was Tintoretto so called?

ART QUIZ NUMBER 2

No, the answer to question number ten isn't the same sort of relief you will feel when you finish this Quiz! (The correct answers are on page 179.)

1. What are gargoyles?
2. Define façade.
3. Name the picture inspired by Keat's poem "Isabel."
4. What is a scarab?
5. Why was Gilbert Stuart's Athenaeum portrait of Washington unfinished?
6. Who is known as the Corot of America?
7. The grapes painted by what ancient artist were so realistic that birds pecked at them?
8. Of whom was it said, "If you would see his monument, look around you?"
9. Was royal purple really a purple color?
10. What is bas-relief?
11. Who was the artist famous for his portraits from the life of American Indians?
12. Name the artists who painted "The Angelus";

"Descent from the Cross"; "Birth of Venus"; "The Horse Fair."

13. In what field did John La Farge have his greatest success?

14. What are the so-called lost arts?

15. For what is the statue "Sleeping Ariadne" famous?

16. Caryatides represent female figures, what are the corresponding male figures?

17. Which is the oldest art?

18. Is Rembrandt's "Night Watch" really a night picture?

19. What Spanish painter is famous for depicting the brilliant glare of sunshine in his pictures?

20. Who did the murals at Rockefeller City?

21. What is Satsuma ware?

22. Is stained glass seen to best advantage on a clear day or a cloudy one?

23. What is the meaning of Bambino?

24. Explain the term "value" in art.

25. In what country is the finest example of Moorish art?

WORLD HISTORY QUIZ NUMBER 1

Don't feel embarrassed! Even Henry the Eighth was hard put to it sometimes to remember the names of all his wives! (Answers to World History Quiz questions are on page 180.)

1. How many signed the Declaration of Independence?
2. Only one of our Presidents was born west of the Mississippi. Who was he?
3. What is the Dail Eireann?
4. Who was the Colonial Governor who had only one leg?
5. What battle in America was fought two weeks after the end of the war?
6. Identify the Olive Branch Petition.
7. To what period does the Hundred Days refer?
8. What American leader demanded the surrender of Fort Ticonderoga "in the name of the Great Jehovah and the Continental Congress?"
9. Name the commoner who was ruler of England.
10. Who was largely responsible for the unification of Germany?

11. Six famous foreigners participated in the American Revolution. Who were they?

12. Which President wrote a History of the United States in 500 words?

13. Tell who the following were: Gustavus Adolphus, Cavour, Homer, Nero.

14. Who was author of the Fourteen Points, and to what did they refer?

15. What happened on St. Bartholomew's Eve?

16. Give the name of the King of England who could speak no English.

17. What was the Battle of the Three Emperors?

18. Name the wives of Henry VIII.

19. Give date and location of the "Battle Above the Clouds."

20. Which of the thirteen original States was named for Queen Elizabeth?

21. Has Washington always been the capital of the United States?

22. What great battle was largely decided by an unseen sunken road?

23. What and where is Manchukuo?

24. Queen Victoria celebrated two jubilees. What were they?

25. What title did Henry of Navarre assume when he became king?

WORLD HISTORY QUIZ NUMBER 2

If you're trying to reduce your percentage, start in on the Diet of Worms! You will be surprised how easy it is to take off four from your score. (Answers on page 181.)

1. Name the first king of all England.
2. Saratoga was the decisive battle of what war?
3. In American history who were the "Little Giants?"
4. The Boer War was precipitated by what raid?
5. To whom was the term "Mossbacks" applied?
6. When was the last battle fought on English soil?
7. What was the Black Hole of Calcutta?
8. Xerxes was the ruler of what people?
9. Who was Queen of England for nine days?
10. In whose administration was the Era of Good Feeling?
11. What happened at Runnymede?
12. To what does the term Big Five refer?
13. Give the term for a sudden overthrow of an existing government?
14. The capture of Jerusalem in the World War was led by what general?
15. Who is the Father of History?

[7]

16. Where is the seat of the League of Nations?
17. What political group in the United States wore as an emblem a button of the Head of the Goddess of Liberty made out of a copper cent?
18. The Polish Corridor is composed of territory belonging formerly to what country?
19. Where did Washington assume command of the Continental Army?
20. Has Norway always been an independent country?
21. In speaking of a "Little Group of Wilful Men," whom did President Wilson mean?
22. For what remarkable feat is Hannibal known?
23. What is meant by the Diet of Worms?
24. In the Constitution where is the Elastic Clause?
25. The Entente Cordiale was a friendly agreement between what nations?

BIOGRAPHY QUIZ NUMBER 1

You don't need to go to a Carnegie Library to learn what American industrialist was known as the Laird of Skibo. (Just turn to page 182 for the right answer!)

1. What European traveler of the Middle Ages is honored by a golden statue in one of China's temples?
2. To what Revolutionary War General was the sobriquet "Swamp Fox" given?
3. Who was the Uncrowned King of Arabia?
4. What happened to Lord Kitchener?
5. Where is the tomb of Mohammed?
6. In what activity was Mussolini formerly engaged?
7. What English traveler disguised himself and made a pilgrimage to Mecca?
8. How did Cleopatra die?
9. Under what pen name did the humorist Charles Farrar Browne write?
10. Has the ex-Kaiser a physical deformity?
11. Identify the Member of Parliament of Jewish birth who said, "I will sit down now, but the time will come when you will hear me?"
12. Who are Einstein and Epstein?

[9]

13. To whom does G.B.S. refer?

14. The words Veni, Vidi, Vici (I came, I saw, I conquered) were used by what famous ruler?

15. Who was Rasputin?

16. What great educator and philosopher fell in love with his pupil?

17. What American woman was called "Princess Alice?"

18. "Laird of Skibo" was the nickname for what American capitalist and manufacturer?

19. What favorite of a Bavarian King died in New York in 1861?

20. Carmen Sylva was the pen name of what royal writer?

21. Name the three husbands of Mary, Queen of Scots.

22. Who is Schiaparelli?

23. With whom were the "Three Marys" connected?

24. Where is John Brown of Ossawatomie buried?

25. An American patriot said, "I regret that I have but one life to give for my country." Who was he?

BIOGRAPHY QUIZ NUMBER 2

Anybody who got in the way of Boadicea's broad-axe would have testified that she was a real person! You're a real person, yourself, if you get 100 in this Quiz! (See page 183 for the right answers.)

1. Who is the present Ambassador to the Court of St. James?
2. Name the first President of the German Republic.
3. What King was assassinated at a masked ball?
4. Who danced for the head of John the Baptist?
5. With what venture was Cyrus Field connected?
6. Name the admiral who rules a kingdom.
7. Who is known as the Builder of South Africa?
8. For what is Froebel famous?
9. What ruler flooded wide areas of his land to check the invaders?
10. Who is said to have singed the King of Spain's beard?
11. Of what nationality was Alexander the Great?
12. In what art did Pavlova excel?
13. What French Revolutionary leader was murdered in his bath? By whom?

14. For what is Nicholas Breakspear noted?
15. Was Boadicea a real person?
16. How old was Princess Elizabeth of England in 1938?
17. Who was the laughing philosopher?
18. What Holy Roman Emperor was distinguished for his red beard?
19. Was de Valera born in Ireland?
20. How did Elbert Hubbard meet his death?
21. What were the last words of Goethe?
22. Name three sisters who became famous as writers.
23. To whom was the nickname "Tiger" given?
24. Name the noted British Admiral who had but one eye.
25. Whose tomb bears the inscription the "Unhappy Queen of England?"

BIBLE QUIZ NUMBER 1

No, Septuagint does not mean a gentleman aged three score and ten years. A hint to Johnny—try this Quiz on your Sunday School teacher! (The answers are on page 184.)

1. How many times does the Lord's Prayer occur in the Bible?
2. What is meant by the Canon in reference to the Bible?
3. Whose ear did Peter cut off?
4. Who became leader of the children of Israel after the death of Moses?
5. The first Temple in Jerusalem was built by what king?
6. Of what wood was the Ark made?
7. How many parables of Jesus Christ's are recorded?
8. To whom was the Land of Goshen given? By whom?
9. Who cursed the day on which he was born?
10. What does Septuagint stand for?
11. The Book of Revelations supplied the title for a famous novel. What was it?

12. Which is the shortest Psalm?

13. Who was fed by the ravens?

14. What is the meaning of Emmanuel?

15. Where does the most famous passage on love in all literature occur?

16. What was Paul's trade?

17. Are the Authorized Version and the King James Bible the same?

18. What became of the Ark of the Covenant?

19. What Jewish ruler visited Jesus by night?

20. Where did Noah's Ark come to rest?

21. For what did Esau sell his birthright?

22. What are the abecedarian Psalms?

23. How long did it take Martin Luther to translate the Bible into German?

24. Who brought a child back to life by breathing into its mouth?

25. How old was Jesus when he began to teach?

BIBLE QUIZ NUMBER 2

We hope you won't be like Lot's wife and turn back to see the answers (page 184) before you've tried your best, or you may be turned into a human salt cellar!

1. Did Jesus leave any written messages?
2. Whom did Saul consult before his last battle with the Philistines?
3. By whom was Jesus baptized?
4. How far was a Sabbath day's journey?
5. Where do you find the Beatitudes?
6. By whom was Sisera killed, and how?
7. What happened to Lot's wife?
8. Which of the Apostles was named the Rock?
9. Who was the king that saw the writing on the wall?
10. A woman anointed Jesus' feet with spikenard. Who was she?
11. How was Elijah taken up to Heaven?
12. What is the Fifth Commandment?
13. Which of the Apostles were brothers?
14. Are any of the original manuscripts of the Bible in existence?
15. Where in the Bible do we find the Golden Rule?

16. To what does Pentateuch refer?
17. Name the four major prophets.
18. Who is meant by the "voice of one crying in the wilderness?"
19. Which of the Gospels is the shortest?
20. How did Paul escape from Damascus?
21. What king of Israel was a poet and musician?
22. How many years did the Jews under Moses wander in the desert?
23. To whom did Jesus first appear after His Resurrection?
24. What is the Vulgate?
25. Define Alpha and Omega.

SPORTS AND GAMES QUIZ NUMBER 1

Question: What is the most popular indoor game today? Answer: The game of Quizzing! Be a good sport, and try your best—and remember you score 4 points for every correct answer. (You'll find the answers on page 185.)

1. When was the first Kentucky Derby run?
2. What is the fastest sport?
3. What was the greatest number of home runs made by Babe Ruth in one season?
4. What British game corresponds to baseball in America?
5. Why is a steeplechase so called?
6. Where is the Golf Capital of America?
7. What are the periods of play in a polo game called?
8. Name the national sport of Spain.
9. In what years have the New York Yankees and New York Giants met in the World Series?
10. What modern game originated among the North American Indians?
11. What is the average weight of a football player's clothes?
12. Why is chess called the royal game?
13. Where was Knute Rockne born?

14. Big Red is the nickname of what race horse?
15. What baseball teams are called the Indians, Senators, Cardinals, Tigers?
16. For what class of boxers is there no weight limit?
17. On what river is the Oxford and Cambridge boat races rowed?
18. Of what is the center of a standard baseball made?
19. What is the fastest swimming stroke?
20. With whom was Tunney's last fight, and when?
21. What famous golfer never took lessons?
22. Who named the English Derby, "Blue Ribbon of the Turf?"
23. In what city were the last Olympic games held?
24. Who was the most valuable player in the American League in 1937?
25. In what year did Gertrude Ederle swim the English Channel?

SPORTS AND GAMES QUIZ NUMBER 2

If you are a close student of the daily sports page you will be able to answer this Quiz in one round. How long is a round? (See page 186.)

1. How tall is Joe Louis?
2. What is the hat trick in cricket?
3. How many umpires are on the field during a World Series game?
4. In playing chess which player has the white men?
5. What is the name of the wicker basket carried by fishermen?
6. Has a horse ever won the English Derby twice?
7. Where was the famous long count fight between Dempsey and Tunney staged?
8. To what sport does slalom refer?
9. In boxing how long is the round?
10. What is meant by a straw house in reference to a circus?
11. With what sport was Sir Thomas Lipton identified?
12. In the game of Poker with all deuces wild, does five of a kind beat a straight flush?
13. What is the best wood for skiis?

14. Who is the Czar of Baseball?
15. In Contract Bridge does a redouble close the bidding?
16. In contract bridge what is a strategic pass?
17. Name some of the famous horses ridden by Jockey Earl Sande.
18. Why is a dead man's hand in poker so-called?
19. With what game is Wimbledon associated?
20. How many points are scored for a touchdown in football?
21. What does the highest hand in cribbage count?
22. To whom did John L. Sullivan lose the heavyweight title in 1897?
23. Why do circus people refer to all clowns as Joey?
24. What is the important stroke in tennis?
25. In dog racing, how far ahead of the dogs is the mechanical rabbit kept?

POLITICS AND GOVERNMENT QUIZ NUMBER 1

What country is ruled by a Shah? Pshaw! That's easy! At least it's easy after you take a peek at the answers on page 186.

1. What is the symbol of authority without which the House of Representatives does not officially convene?
2. Tell the significance of Left and Right as applied to political parties.
3. How many States were represented at the first Continental Congress?
4. What is the Kingdom of Hellas?
5. Did the District of Columbia ever have a delegate in Congress?
6. Who was the Vice-Presidential candidate when Taft ran the second time?
7. Who suggested the Monroe Doctrine?
8. For how long a term is the President of France elected?
9. When did the South first vote solidly Democratic in a Presidential election?
10. How long has the word boss been used in politics?

11. How many Presidents have died in office?

12. When an Act is passed by Congress over the President's veto can the President take any further action?

13. Approximately how many people does one Congressman represent?

14. Which Senator has had the longest continuous service?

15. What country is ruled by a Shah?

16. Who was the "Cowboy Congressman?"

17. What States do not have a direct primary system?

18. Is it necessary that the Speaker be a member of the House of Representatives?

19. How old is the Nazi organization?

20. Is applause permitted in the Senate galleries in Washington?

21. What was the Wilmot Proviso?

22. Albion was the ancient name for what country?

23. On which side of the chamber do the Democrats sit in the House of Representatives?

24. Where was the late Representative Zioncheck born?

25. What happens to the original copy of a bill after it is signed?

POLITICS AND GOVERNMENT QUIZ NUMBER 2

Politicians are barred from taking this Quiz. It is a wise rule, anyway, for politicians never to answer any questions. (Answers on page 187.)

1. Has the United States recognized Soviet Russia?
2. Did a President ever address Congress at night?
3. How many women are in the British Parliament?
4. Distinguish between a *de facto* and a *de jure* government.
5. Must a Congressman be present a certain per cent of the time Congress is in session?
6. Who was the last survivor of the Continental Congress?
7. Which is the older of our two major parties?
8. Is God mentioned in the Constitution of the United States?
9. Are Supreme Court Justices elected?
10. How many families have been represented twice in the White House?
11. Oligarchy is what type of government?
12. By what name is the British financial minister known?

13. Name the smallest independent state in the world.

14. Who nominated Hoover for President in 1920?

15. Are all the Justices of the United States Supreme Court Americans by birth?

16. What is the title of the ruler of Belgium?

17. Who was the youngest man ever nominated for President by a major party in this country?

18. Which Province is guaranteed a representation of 65 in the Canadian House of Commons?

19. To what does the term "slush fund" refer?

20. What States have neither Republican nor Democratic Governors?

21. Who was the first man appointed to the United States Supreme Court?

22. Is it true that there were Presidents of the United States before George Washington?

23. What noted British Prime Minister died aboard ship in 1937?

24. Who is the youngest member of the Supreme Court?

25. What President was buried without funeral services?

NATURAL HISTORY QUIZ NUMBER 1

Don't forget to wear a sprig of Myosotis in your button hole, and you'll find yourself a whiz at this Quiz. What is a Myosotis? See page 188.

1. What four-footed animal cannot walk?
2. Name the largest family of plants.
3. What small animal is said to resemble the elephant?
4. Is coral, animal, vegetable or mineral?
5. Who originated the modern system of classifying plants and animals?
6. To what does the name John Dory refer?
7. Which is the cleanest animal?
8. Do animals grow during hibernation?
9. What animal has red perspiration?
10. The tallest bird can grow to a height of 8 feet, what is it?
11. How much of the watermelon is water?
12. What reptile squirts blood from its eyes?
13. Why is the compass plant so-called?
14. What animal is noted for building dams?
15. Myosotis is the botanical name for what popular flower?

16. Is a live lobster red?
17. Are there any birds that can reverse their wing action?
18. What portions of the avocado, asparagus and artichoke are eaten as food?
19. Give the words for a multitude of sheep, partridges, fish, locusts.
20. Is the ground color of zebra white or black?
21. What class of animals are equally at home on land or in water?
22. How do truffles grow?
23. Why don't trees continue to grow taller as long as they live?
24. What mammal is able to fly?
25. Sea birds provide what valuable fertilizer?

NATURAL HISTORY QUIZ NUMBER 2

Are you feeling all hot and bothered? Just wave your ears and be cool and comfortable. The elephant does—and the elephant never forgets. In case you have forgotten, see page 188.

1. What animal lives the longest?
2. What domestic animal cannot reproduce itself?
3. What living creatures predominate in the world?
4. Besides the elephant, what three animals provide ivory?
5. To what plant family does garlic belong?
6. In what country are storks protected by law?
7. What mammal can live longest without water?
8. How many times its own weight can an ant carry?
9. What are cavies?
10. In what way is the larch peculiar?
11. Does the male or female mosquito bite?
12. What tree is named for one of Jesus' disciples?
13. Why is the railway beetle so-called?
14. What bird kicks its prey to death?
15. Is there a tree that is cut by the light of the moon?
16. Leveret is the young of what animal?

17. What animal common in the South is related to the kangaroo?
18. Why does an elephant wave its ears?
19. What bird leaves its eggs to hatch themselves in the sun?
20. Fungi are distinguished by what characteristic?
21. What bird is still trained by the Chinese to catch fish?
22. What is the lowest form of animal life?
23. To what does marsupial refer?
24. Is the sapwood of the ebony black or white?
25. Are sponges plants or animals?

LITERATURE AND LANGUAGE QUIZ
NUMBER 1

Speaking of Palindromes—Oh-oh, we've spilled the answer to Number 13. But do you remember the one—"Able was I ere I saw Elba"? (The answers to this Quiz may be found on page 189.)

1. What book is the best seller of all times?
2. Who was the author who predicted the submarine many years ago?
3. In which historical novel is there a famous chariot race?
4. What letter of the alphabet is used most often?
5. Who said, "Everybody talks about the weather but no one does anything about it?"
6. What hero of a drama was sensitive about the size of his nose?
7. How many languages are there in the world?
8. Which of Dickens' novels is said to be largely biographical?
9. Where is the Poet's Corner?
10. Who was the Sage of Concord?
11. Which of the universal languages has had the greatest success?

12. What common article of clothing derives its name from a poem by Burns?

13. What is the name for a line that reads the same both ways like "Madam I'm Adam?"

14. Which poet wrote his own epitaph, and what is it?

15. Who is the English physician author of a current best-seller?

16. Are the words, "Cleanliness is next to Godliness" found in the Bible?

17. What British author holds a high position in Colonial government?

18. Name the shortest poem in English.

19. What was Voltaire's real name?

20. How many sounds are there in the English language?

21. What book of Herman Melville led to the abolition of flogging in the Navy?

22. Who are some of the well-known lovers in literature?

23. What is the derivation of the word alphabet?

24. What member of Congress wrote a poem about Mrs. Roosevelt?

25. Who created the character of Mr. Dooley?

LITERATURE AND LANGUAGE QUIZ NUMBER 2

William Makepeace Thackeray wrote: "he quizzed unmercifully all the men in the room." So you can see that they were doing it a hundred years ago! See page 190.

1. What father and son were both famous writers?
2. Name the American journalist of foreign birth who became a Japanese citizen?
3. "The American Commonwealth" was written by what famous Englishman?
4. Define "Bowdlerize."
5. What successful author did not begin to write until he was over 65?
6. Where do we get the term ugly duckling?
7. Who said, "There is no royal road to learning?"
8. Was there really a Man Without a Country?
9. Whence do we get Brer Rabbit and Brer Fox?
10. By whom was the saying "Taxation without representation is tyranny" first used?
11. Name a famous living Hindu writer.
12. What was Mark Twain's real name?
13. Name the Three Musketeers.

14. What English novelist of foreign birth is said to have written the best English of his day?

15. What American author is noted for the unexpected endings to his short stories?

16. Is there a children's classic that is at the same time a biting satire on the human race?

17. What was Kipling's first name?

18. Was it Napoleon who called the English a nation of shopkeepers?

19. What character of Shakespeare has the most lines to speak?

20. In such titles as "Ye Old Ship," how is "ye" pronounced?

21. What great poem was written while the author was in prison?

22. In what famous short story is the conclusion left to the reader?

23. Did Shelley die a natural death?

24. How many languages are spoken in Switzerland?

25. What words contain all of the vowels?

MUSIC QUIZ NUMBER 1

You may remember what composer was known as "Papa," but you'll say "Uncle" before you've answered all of the questions in Music Quiz Number One. In case you're a bit off key turn to page 191.

1. Name the Signer of the Declaration of Independence who was a noted musician.
2. The tone of which musical instrument most nearly resembles the human voice?
3. Which composer was familiarly known as Papa?
4. What is a chorale, and who first used it?
5. To what historical events does Tschaikowsky's Overture 1812 refer?
6. Who was the Poet of the Piano?
7. What American play is the subject of an opera by Puccini?
8. Where was the home of the Meistersingers?
9. About how long does a popular song remain a hit?
10. By what term are the different sections of an orchestra known?
11. What is a "pop" concert?
12. Name the Brazilian grand opera singer now with the Metropolitan.

13. What famous musician walked 150 miles to study music?
14. Did Beethoven compose most of his great symphonies before or after he became deaf?
15. What is close harmony?
16. The daughter of what famous singer recently published a musical novel?
17. Who was the March King?
18. What instruments are popularly associated with Spanish folk music?
19. What musical instrument was invented by Benjamin Franklin?
20. What operas comprise the Ring of the Nibelung?
21. The armies led by Joan of Arc had a favorite hymn, what was it?
22. Who was the German musician who received a royal appointment in England?
23. How did the tune "Old Hundred" get its name?
24. Libretto is what part of an opera?
25. What Viennese composer was noted for his melodious songs?

MUSIC QUIZ NUMBER 2

If we told you that the correct answer to Question Number One is twice the score each correct answer receives, then how old is Anne? (Check your answers with page 191.)

1. The usual range in popular songs is how many notes?
2. Who composed "The Flight of the Bumble Bee?"
3. In what opera does the song "Caro-Nome" occur?
4. What is the most popular march in American music?
5. Samisen is the musical instrument of what nation?
6. Who is considered the greatest Finnish composer?
7. On what opera was Puccini working when he died? Was it produced?
8. With what great musician is the town of Bayreuth associated?
9. The widow of what American composer established a colony for musicians?
10. Which single instrument can be made to represent a whole orchestra?
11. Why is the Czardas so called?
12. Is the opera "Rigoletto" based on a novel?

13. Did Walter Damrosch write an opera?
14. What is the most famous symphony with a choral part?
15. Who composed "Alexander's Ragtime Band;" "Deep River," "Oh! Susannah?"
16. A bagpipe player is the hero of what opera?
17. For what piece is Maurice Ravel best known?
18. Which musical instrument reaches the highest note?
19. Who is the Father of the Symphony?
20. What does a capella mean?
21. Has the city of Rome been made the subject of any famous compositions?
22. Who is the present conductor of the New York Philharmonic Orchestra?
23. Who composed the music to "H.M.S. Pinafore?"
24. For what composition is General Daniel Butterfield famous?
25. What is the national hymn of Canada?

FAMILIAR SAYINGS QUIZ

By this time you may agree with Casca, the Roman, who said it was all Greek to him, but somebody actually did make each of these wisecracks once! Page 192 for the guilty parties.

1. "A thing of beauty is a joy forever."
2. "To see ourselves as others see us."
3. "He prayeth best who loveth best."
4. "A little knowledge is a dangerous thing."
5. "Down to the sea in ships."
6. "Eternal vigilance is the price of liberty."
7. "It is no time for mirth or laughter, the cold, gray dawn of the morning after."
8. "Lips that touch liquor shall never touch mine."
9. "A rose by any other name would smell as sweet."
10. "The road to hell is paved with good intentions."
11. "What's the Constitution between friends?"
12. "There is nothing new under the sun."
13. "Let George do it."
14. "Life's just one damned thing after another."
15. "I escaped with the skin of my teeth."
16. "It's all Greek to me."

17. "It's much easier to be critical than to be correct."
18. "I do not agree with one word you say but will defend with my life your right to say it."
19. "Fly in the ointment."
20. "Tell me what you eat and I will tell you what you are."
21. "Go west, young man!"
22. "Happy warrior."
23. "Brain trust."
24. "Even Steven."
25. "There is so much good in the worst of us."

SCIENCE QUIZ NUMBER 1

There may be someone who will insist that the answer to Question seventeen is his own cranium! For the correct answers to this Quiz, see page 193.

1. Is it true that there is in the eye a spot where you can't see?
2. Where is the windiest place on earth?
3. Which has the fastest current, a straight river or a crooked one?
4. Why are bridges painted with red paint?
5. Why doesn't it kill birds to roost on an electric wire?
6. Which is the most abundant metal?
7. Where is the place where the date changes?
8. Which are the three predominating colors in flowers?
9. Of what is dry ice made?
10. Where in the United States is the heaviest snowfall?
11. What is disorientation?
12. With what is Charles Darwin mainly identified?
13. When was Halley's comet last seen?

14. How often does Halley's comet appear?
15. Is the earth nearer the sun in summer or in winter?
16. Which is hotter, red hot or white hot?
17. Give the name for the solid portion of the earth.
18. Which is the heaviest metal?
19. Does coal oil come from coal?
20. When crossing the Atlantic from England to America do you set your watch back or forward?
21. Where is the stratosphere?
22. Approximately how far are we from the sun?
23. What is the eye of a storm?
24. For what is the Baumé scale used?
25. Can a rainbow be seen at night?

SCIENCE QUIZ NUMBER 2

You will laugh when you look up (on page 193) the answer to Question Number Thirteen!

1. What planets have satellites?
2. Which animal makes no sound?
3. Who devised the periodic system of the chemical elements?
4. What is the most important factor of soil erosion?
5. Explain neap tide.
6. Where in the world does the greatest rainfall occur?
7. Name the so-called simple machines.
8. How many constellations are there?
9. What gas exhaled by animals is utilized by plants?
10. Is lightning zigzag?
11. What element is necessary to make a fire burn?
12. Insulin is used in the treatment of what disease?
13. Give the common name for nitrous oxide.
14. Is the Milky Way always visible in the sky?
15. Is the surface of water in a container flat?
16. What valuable fiber is obtained from rocks?
17. Give the three fundamental units of measure.

18. Which is the only metal that is liquid at ordinary temperatures?
19. What substance was used to coat the disk of the 200-inch telescope?
20. Why is there a gap between rails of a railway track?
21. For what is the anemometer used?
22. What turns blue litmus red?
23. When is the moon gibbous?
24. Which element was discovered on the sun before it was found on earth?
25. What is a phobia?

GEOGRAPHY QUIZ NUMBER 1

If you can go around the world in eight days, surely it oughtn't to take more than eight minutes to answer these twenty-five questions. (Correct answers on page 194.)

1. Is the Atlantic or Pacific end of the Panama Canal the farthest east?
2. What State is divided into parishes instead of counties?
3. What are the seven political divisions of Central America?
4. Why is the equator so called?
5. Where in the United States is the city that had a population of 10,000 on the day it was settled?
6. Name the countries that border France.
7. What great city is built upon seven hills?
8. Give the former name of Oslo. Of what country is it the capital?
9. What is the highest steam navigated lake in the world?
10. In what country is the southernmost city in the world?
11. Is the Mississippi or the Missouri the longer river?

12. Who first announced the belief that the world is round?

13. In what country is Mont Blanc?

14. Who was the Pathfinder of the Seas?

15. From what country do we get most of our coffee?

16. For what are the following noted: Grand Banks, Detroit, Tuskegee, Agra, the Shetland Islands, St. Moritz?

17. Is Canada larger or smaller than the United States not including Alaska?

18. Is there a desert in New England?

19. What is the most densely populated country in the world?

20. Locate Papua, Cuzco, Pend Oreille, Jungfrau, Scutari, Nantucket.

21. What is Pisa's most celebrated building?

22. Where are the highest and lowest points in the United States?

23. To whom do the Azores belong?

24. What active volcano has the largest crater?

25. Khyber Pass connects what two countries?

GEOGRAPHY QUIZ NUMBER 2

Not only is there a town named "Hell," but there is a place named "Hell," and right now you probably are wishing we were there! (You'll find the answers on page 195.)

1. Name the State which has 10,000 lakes.
2. What is Gdynia?
3. Can you name the oldest inhabited city in the world?
4. Locate Ausable Chasm, Garden of the Gods, Mt. Rubidoux, The Natural Bridge, Starved Rock.
5. Define treaty port.
6. The largest bay in the world is part of what ocean?
7. In what city is the Miracle Mile?
8. Which continent extends furthest south?
9. Which States have the highest and lowest average elevation respectively?
10. Is there really a town named Hell?
11. Name the countries that compose Scandinavia?
12. What does U.S.S.R. stand for?
13. Where is the famous city square noted for its pigeons?
14. Locate the Côte d'Azur.

15. Name the world's greatest cotton port.
16. For what is Trinidad noted?
17. What great river has no tributary for 2000 miles?
18. Which is the Holy City of the Hindus?
19. Give another name for Korea.
20. Of what group of islands is Funchal the capital?
21. Name the great geographer of the ancient world.
22. What and where are the Fens?
23. What great city of Europe is said to be built on bones?
24. Honolulu harbor has a famous landmark, what is it?
25. Where is the mountain named in honor of Nurse Edith Cavell?

ABBREVIATIONS QUIZ

Your brain will have to make quite a few R.P.M. in order to get 100 P.C. in this one. N.B. that the correct answers are not F.O.B. the C.Z, but on page 195 I.B.O.T.B. (in back of the book).

1. MSS.
2. Cantab.
3. B.A.
4. A 1.
5. Lb.
6. Ult.
7. Sc.
8. C.S.A.
9. D.G.
10. r.p.m.
11. L. s. d.
12. N.B.
13. B.B.C.
14. A.M.
15. Viz.
16. F.O.B.
17. P.P.C.

18. i.e.
19. A.D.C.
20. P.I.
21. dwt.
22. S.P.C.C.
23. A.A.A.S.
24. Bart.
25. C.Z.

MYTHOLOGY QUIZ

Those who are inclined to feel that there is a lot of bull in the classics will be surprised at the answer to Question Number 24. (See page 196.)

1. Who had the golden touch?
2. Name the household gods.
3. Who fell in love with himself?
4. Whose body was invulnerable except for the heel?
5. What was Sisyphus' task in the lower world?
6. Of what was Vulcan the god?
7. Why did the gods live on nectar and ambrosia?
8. How did the giants try to reach heaven?
9. Ormuzd was the supreme deity of what people?
10. Who made himself wings and learned to fly?
11. For whom is Friday named?
12. What golden fruit was cast among the gods, inscribed, "For the fairest?"
13. What powers were ascribed to Circe?
14. Who were Charon and Chiron?
15. Who wept incessantly?
16. What did the Gorgon's head do?

17. Identify Nokomis.
18. What was Valhalla?
19. Name the heavenly twins who helped the Romans in battle.
20. How did Theseus find his way out of the Labyrinth?
21. Who fell in love with Psyche?
22. By whom were dragon's teeth sown?
23. What device was used by the Greeks to enter Troy?
24. Into what animal did Jupiter turn Io?
25. How did Janus differ from other gods?

AMERICAN HISTORY QUIZ
NUMBER 1

Just because you are a "100 per cent American" doesn't mean that you will get 100 per cent in this Quiz! (You'll know where you stand when you look at page 196.)

1. Who left his horse and plough in the field and hastened to join the army?
2. What famous treaty was made under an elm tree?
3. Name the States that had two capitals. What were they?
4. Which was the first State to secede?
5. What colony exiled a man who advocated religious freedom?
6. How did Alexander Hamilton die?
7. Who commanded the Mexicans in the War 1846–1848?
8. In what great battle did two famous generals die?
9. What was the first military engagement of the Civil War?
10. Name the three Englishmen who supported the American Colonial cause.
11. Who is said to have used the words, "Millions for defense but not one cent for tribute?"

12. Which of the states bought another state?

13. In what war was the city of Washington burned?

14. Who was the opponent of Abraham Lincoln in the famous debates over the slave question?

15. To whom was the nickname Light-Horse Harry given?

16. What State first granted suffrage to women?

17. In which State was Andrew Jackson born?

18. What fateful act was known as the Mother of Mischief?

19. Where was the Lost Colony planted?

20. How did America come to be so named?

21. Who was President of the Confederacy?

22. With what affair was John Slidell connected?

23. "Return to normalcy" is associated with what President?

24. What vessel, sunk in Santiago Harbor, precipitated a war with Spain?

25. Which great Southerner was offered command of the Union Forces at the outbreak of the Civil War?

AMERICAN HISTORY QUIZ
NUMBER 2

We knew there was a man named Franklin, a stove named Franklin, and an Institute named Franklin,—but a State? Let's look and see on page 197.

1. Was there ever a State named Franklin?
2. What did General Prescott tell his men before the Battle of Bunker Hill?
3. Which of the Southern States was a non-slave State during the Civil War?
4. Who preceded Franklin Pierce, President of the United States?
5. To whom was the nickname "Old Fuss and Feathers" given?
6. Who made a famous oration known as the "Reply to Hayne" in the U. S. Senate in 1830?
7. Who was the Scotsman who served in the United States Navy and subsequently in the Russian Navy?
8. When did we acquire Alaska? From whom?
9. In what battle did Pickett's charge occur?
10. What great American is said to have arrived in Philadelphia with a loaf of bread under his arm?
11. Which President learned to read and write after his marriage?

12. The "Open Door" in China is identified with which American statesman?

13. Who is said to have visited the east coast of North America about A.D. 1000?

14. By whom was Aguinaldo, leader of the Philippine Insurrection, captured?

15. To whom are attributed the words, "Now Gentlemen, we must all hang together, or we shall hang separately?"

16. To whose words are we indebted for our term Spoils System?

17. Give the name of the companion of William Clark on his western expedition.

18. Who was author of the command "Disperse you rebels, lay down your arms?" To whom was it given?

19. What is the name of the family of artists who painted the portraits of so many of the Fathers of the Country?

20. Who said, "I purpose to fight it out on this line if it takes all summer?"

21. The Great Triumvirate included what great men?

22. By whom was the American fleet commanded in the Battle of Manila Bay?

23. Who was the American statesman who was grandson of a king?

24. What was the name given to the arrangement for assisting runaway slaves to escape?

25. What was the Billy Bowlegs War?

RADIO QUIZ

There are several popular "Quiz Hours" on the radio. We hope some of the questions in our book will help you to win a prize. (Answers to Radio Quiz on page 197.)

1. Which is the most desirable time to broadcast a program?
2. Name some announcers who have received awards for diction.
3. With what call letters do all commercial radio stations in this country begin?
4. What was Roxy's real name?
5. Which States have the most radio stations?
6. Name three programs that have been on the air a long time.
7. What is the theme song of the Chesterfield hour?
8. Explain electrical transcriptions.
9. Who writes Charlie McCarthy's dialogue?
10. Who was the first President to speak over the radio?
11. Does Amos or Andy take the part of Brother Crawford?
12. How long is the usual radio contract period?

13. Where is the most powerful radio station?
14. Is "The Big Show" by Jerome Kern the theme song of the Jello, Firestone, Chase and Sanborn or Ford program?
15. What does DX mean?
16. Why is a radio log so called?
17. Which noted comedian has five daughters?
18. What are the two types of radio programs?
19. Name the well-known radio character created by Phillips Lord.
20. What do the letters A.S.C.A.P. stand for?
21. Who is the Flying Commentator?
22. Name the famous young pupil of Andres de Segurola.
23. Who always speaks for the character he created?
24. What natural wonder is the theme song of a radio program?
25. Who is Asa Yoelson?

MOTION PICTURE QUIZ

What Disney character expresses the way we feel in the midst of a Relativity Quiz? Could it be Dopey? For Robert Taylor's sure-enough name see page 198.

1. How long did it take Walt Disney to make "Snow White and the Seven Dwarfs?"
2. Approximately how many people are employed in the motion picture industry?
3. Who won the Motion Picture Academy Award both in 1936 and 1937?
4. What was the first movie with a plot?
5. Explain the significance of the letters A.S.C. used after a camera man's name.
6. Who is Mrs. Arthur Hornblow?
7. What popular play was sold to the movies for a quarter of a million dollars?
8. Who made the first newsreel?
9. What comedian is associated with a golf links scene?
10. Who are Pauline Levy, Margaret Fitzpatrick, Raymond Guion?
11. What popular actress of stage and screen attended Bryn Mawr?

12. Name the star whose real name is Bickel, and who was once a student at the University of Wisconsin.

13. What famous actress is married to William A. Brady?

14. Where was George Arliss born?

15. For what film did director Frank Capra receive the Movie Award?

16. Who was the heroine in the early serial "Exploits of Elaine?"

17. Whose real name is Spangler Arlington Brugh?

18. In what type of picture do Buck Jones, Ken Maynard, Tim McCoy play?

19. Who first used close-ups?

20. Where was Bela Lugosi born?

21. Can you recall the name of the Japanese actor who was so popular some years ago?

22. Where did Douglas Fairbanks, Sr., attend college?

23. How did .Hollywood receive its name?

24. What is the name of a famous woman director?

25. Are the MGM Studios in Hollywood?

MATHEMATICS QUIZ

No, an acre foot isn't what you have after a horse steps on your big toe. See page 198.

1. What are the prime numbers under 25?
2. What do G.C.D. and L.C.M. stand for?
3. Define isosceles triangle.
4. How many degrees in a circle?
5. Who invented logarithms?
6. How is one duodecillion written?
7. Give the mathematical name for a solid shaped like a doughnut.
8. What is the rule of three?
9. Define perfect number.
10. Can an angle be trisected by means of a straight edge and compass?
11. What does the word geometry mean?
12. How many dimensions has a line?
13. The formula πr^2 represents what?
14. What Roman numeral represents 900?
15. What is the fundamental standard of length in the United States?
16. How many plane surfaces has a wedge?

17. Define acre foot.
18. What is an aliquot part?
19. Dunces rarely get over a certain theorem of Euclid's without stumbling, what is it?
20. A number in a series, that has as many numbers preceding it as following it, is known as what?
21. What is a verst?
22. Abacus was a calculating device used by what people?
23. Which of our ordinals is of French origin?
24. Where did Arabic numerals originate?
25. Give two ways of finding the area of a triangle.

DRAMA QUIZ

Anyone who has a nose for the theatre (not necessarily Cyrano de Bergerac) can answer these very dramatic questions. (If you can't, there's always page 199.)

1. For what role is Walter Hampden noted?
2. To whom is Katharine Cornell married?
3. Why is the Green Room so called?
4. Who popularized the lines "That's all there is— there isn't any more?"
5. "Present Indicative" is the autobiography of what famous playwright and actor?
6. What is No Drama?
7. Why is an actor called a Thespian?
8. Name five plays that have had exceptionally long runs.
9. What actress is remembered for her parts in "Little Minister," "Peter Pan," "A Kiss for Cinderella?"
10. Who was known as the Jersey Lily?
11. Which is Shakespeare's shortest play?
12. What is the family name of the Barrymores?
13. Where is David Garrick buried?
14. What is the name used for dramas that are written to be read and not acted?

15. Name the three dramatic unities.
16. Who wrote "Abie's Irish Rose?"
17. Who was the Tragic Muse?
18. What famous actor was noted for the role of "Dr. Jekyll and Mr. Hyde?"
19. Who are the best known pantomimists of today?
20. Name the actor associated with lariat throwing.
21. The daughter of which noted actor is a monologuist?
22. What producer is noted for his streamlined Shakespearean dramas?
23. Who are Nathan Birbaum and Jack Kubelsky?
24. What American theatrical producer affected clerical garb?
25. Concerning which of our Presidents did an English author write a play?

NEWSPAPER QUIZ

What's black and white, yet read all over? You won't find the answer to that one on page 200!

1. San Simeon is the home of what well-known newspaper publisher?
2. Give the name of the only woman editor and publisher of a metropolitan daily in the United States.
3. For what do the familiar initials AP stand?
4. Who was well-known as Marse Henry?
5. What is the oldest publishers' and advertisers' magazine in the United States?
6. The oldest syndicate feature is advice to the lovelorn, who writes it?
7. Who is continuing the work of the late O. O. McIntyre?
8. What editor at the time of his death in 1936 was the highest paid newspaper man in the country?
9. Who are the creators of: (1) "Bringing Up Father"; (2) "Little Jimmy"; (3) "Krazy Kat"?
10. Which periodical was the first to be called a magazine?
11. Why are stars used on the covers of some magazines?

12. What magazine gave a prize of $50,000 for its present name?

13. Estimate the number of words in a newspaper like the *New York Times*.

14. What is meant by a Sob Sister?

15. What was the name of the A.E.F. paper?

16. Which American paper has the largest circulation?

17. What are tabloids?

18. *Godey's Lady's Book* is noteworthy for what reason?

19. For what does A.B.C. stand in newspaper parlance?

20. A famous inventor started his career as a railroad newsboy, who was he?

21. What is a by-line?

22. What newspaper is distributed free in a Southern city every day on which the sun does not shine?

23. Which newspaper is famous for its Agony Column?

24. Name the colonial newspaper of which many reproductions have been made. Why?

25. How far back does the history of newspapers go?

LAW QUIZ

It will take a "Philadelphia lawyer" to get a perfect score in this one. And even he will have to resort to a misfeasance to do it! (Answers on page 200.)

1. How does common law differ from statutory law?
2. What is a misfeasance?
3. Name the only Province in Canada whose laws are based on the Code Napoleon.
4. When a person is commanded to appear at a certain place on a certain day as witness, what does he receive?
5. What book is essential in every trial court room in the U. S.?
6. In law, what is an infant?
7. What term is applied to the persistent incitement of litigation?
8. What is dower right?
9. Who is Chief Justice of the Supreme Court?
10. How was the Volstead Act distinguished from the 18th Amendment?
11. Are there any national divorce laws in this country?
12. What British law was popularly known as Dora?

13. Give the term for legal rights of owners of land bordering a river or lake.
14. What is the fundamental law of the United States?
15. For what length of time does copyright extend?
16. When a person dies intestate, what does it mean?
17. Where were the earliest blue laws in force in this country?
18. What is an Enoch Arden law?
19. To what does the expression "Twelve Tables" refer?
20. How did the curfew laws originate?
21. For whom were the Baumes Laws named?
22. What does "jus in rem" include?
23. Was there ever a law where the use of a comma caused any misunderstanding of the true meaning of the law?
24. How many laws have been passed by Congress?
25. What is a tort?

TRAVEL QUIZ

Anyone stranded in the midst of a Travel Quiz should ask his directions from a Travel Aide, and then just to be sure should consult page 201.

1. What famous western caverns were discovered by millions of bats issuing from the entrance?
2. Where is "The World's Playground"?
3. By what name is the Paris subway known?
4. Where are the Shenandoah National Park; Old Faithful Geyser; The Finger Lakes; Lake Tahoe?
5. Is there a city noted for its Silver Street?
6. Where is the Chateau Frontenac?
7. Locate the Dismal Swamp.
8. Who operates the Great White Fleet?
9. Name the islands, noted as a resort, that prohibit automobiles.
10. The Loop is the downtown business section of what city?
11. Where are: Multnomah Falls; Mt. Desert; Wayside Inn; El Capitan?
12. What countries are generally included in the Grand Tour?

13. Over which international boundary line is there the most travel?
14. What is the English name for Firenze?
15. In what cities are (1) Bond Street; (2) Unter den Linden; (3) the Prater?
16. In what country can you sail in a dahibijeh?
17. Where would you go to see the Trossachs?
18. What is the favorite shore resort of Venice?
19. Where do people ride in jaunting cars?
20. What do visitors to Norway hope to see?
21. If you wanted to sail on the largest British ship afloat, what would it be? The largest French ship?
22. By whom was the Golden Gate named?
23. How would you expect to travel about in Venice?
24. Is there a Pink City?
25. What steamship line operates the *Rex?*

WORLD WAR QUIZ

If Mata-Hari did not commit hari-kari, then where does that leave bari-bari? The answer will be very, very evident on page 202.

1. Who commanded the A.E.F.
2. Did the German Army ever approach close to Paris?
3. What were the nicknames of the American, British and French soldiers?
4. When did the American troops actually get into action?
5. Name the most popular war song of the English.
6. Who was recognized as the outstanding American hero of the World War?
7. How did the British soldiers refer to their homeland?
8. Who was placed in command of all the Allied Armies?
9. What term was used to designate the moment of attack?
10. Were any battles fought on German soil?
11. What three famous royal houses lost their thrones as a result of the World War?

12. What happened to Alsace-Lorraine at the close of the World War?

13. Who used the phrase "a war to end war?"

14. Did the United States ask for any reparations after the World War?

15. When did Congress declare war?

16. What were some of the important battles of the World War in which American soldiers took part?

17. When and where were the "Fourteen Points" stated by President Wilson?

18. Had the Kaiser abdicated before the Armistice?

19. What position did George Creel hold during the World War?

20. What was the Lost Battalion?

21. Where did the phrase, "Too proud to fight" originate?

22. How many men lost their lives among the 15 belligerent nations in the World War?

23. How did the expression "The world must be made safe for democracy" originate?

24. What happened to the German spy Mata-Hari?

25. What was the exact hour the Armistice went into effect?

BUSINESS QUIZ

Here's a Quiz just for that forgotten man—the Business Man. He will find the answers in the back of the ledger —page 203.

1. In what kind of shop was Mrs. Franklin D. Roosevelt interested?
2. Who originated mail order merchandising?
3. What American merchant founded London's largest department store?
4. Is the largest business in the world an American one?
5. How many kinds of bankruptcy are there?
6. What is the term for one whose name appears in the firm name but who takes no active part in the conduct of the business?
7. What firm began the chain store system?
8. What is a tickler file?
9. Give another name for amanuensis.
10. What merchant formulated twelve rules for success?
11. Did installment selling originate in this country?
12. The largest selling article of a mail order house is what commodity?

13. To whose ingenuity do we owe the Piggly-Wiggly self-service idea?

14. Who is Roger Ward Babson?

15. Name the two credit rating organizations that recently combined.

16. The son of which President of the United States was president of the Pullman Company?

17. For what business are the following noted: Akron, Ohio; Lynn, Massachusetts; Grand Rapids, Michigan; Syracuse; Kansas City; Pittsburgh?

18. What name is given to that period early in the 19th century which marked the replacing of hand labor by machinery?

19. What is the function of an actuary?

20. Which State leads in total income from manufacturing?

21. Define fiscal year.

22. Give the term applied to the periodical swings of business activity.

23. Who stands between the manufacturer and the consumer?

24. For what do C.I.F. and E. and O.E. stand?

25. In what business are the following engaged: (1) Filene's; (2) Sherwin-Williams; (3) Yardley's; (4) Lloyd's?

AERONAUTICS QUIZ

You may find yourself up in the air when you try to locate the answers to these plane and fancy interrogations. Happy landings—on page 203!

1. Who invented the autogiro?
2. What famous aviator was piloting the plane in which Will Rogers was killed?
3. In what year did Colonel Charles A. Lindbergh make his famous flight from the United States to Paris?
4. Was Lindbergh the first man to fly across the Atlantic?
5. Who made the first flight in a heavier-than-air, motor-driven plane?
6. How big is the ordinary parachute?
7. Who commanded the mass airplane flight from Italy to Chicago in 1933?
8. Who was the scientist who ascended 10 miles into the stratosphere in an aluminum sphere attached to a balloon?
9. Who made the first flight over the English Channel?

10. What Government agency regulates commercial aviation in the United States?
11. What is an amphibian plane?
12. What is the name of the body to which the wings of an airplane are attached?
13. What is a hangar?
14. What is soaring?
15. Who was the first woman to fly from Hawaii to San Francisco?
16. How long did the first American transcontinental flight take?
17. What gas did the *Hindenburg* use?
18. Name three large American dirigibles which have crashed.
19. What was Mrs. Lindbergh's maiden name?
20. Where is the Navy flying school?
21. Where did the Wright brothers make their first flight in a motor-driven plane?
22. In what year was the first balloon ascent in America made?
23. Whose plane was the *Lady Southern Cross?*
24. Who commanded the *Graf Zeppelin's* world flight in 1929?
25. What country has a monopoly on helium?

FESTIVALS AND HOLIDAYS QUIZ

April Fool's Day is the feast day of all Quizzers. Not that one has to wait until April 1st in order to feel foolish. Just turn to page 204 and see how you feel!

1. On what day are trees planted?
2. Name the first day of Lent.
3. What celebration derives its name from the Hebrew word yobel, meaning ram's horn?
4. In what country is the Festival of Dolls observed?
5. Why are Red Letter days so named?
6. To whom is the founding of Mother's Day attributed?
7. Define Sabbatical Year.
8. Where is the Tournament of Roses held? When?
9. What people have a kite-flying festival?
10. The British celebrate an historical event on November 5th, what is it?
11. What is the meaning of Epiphany?
12. Which of our words for feasting and merry-making means, in Latin, "Farewell Meat?"
13. What is another name for Candlemas?
14. On what date is International Labor Day observed?

15. Which Saint is commemorated on the day of his birth rather than on that of his death?

16. What were the Twelve Nights?

17. On what day do French unmarried girls pay tribute to the patron saint of old maids?

18. When is the Hebrew Feast of the Trumpets?

19. The people of what nation honor the Kitchen God?

20. What does France's Fête National commemorate?

21. The Welsh people are known for their Eisteddfod, what is it?

22. Who was Saint Swithin?

23. What day in England may be said to correspond to our Mother's Day?

24. Maritime Day, May 22, is the anniversary of what event?

25. What is the national holiday of Canada?

EDUCATION QUIZ

Don't let the name of this Quiz scare you! As far back as the time of Socrates in ancient Greece they were using the Quiz or question-and-answer method of teaching. (Answers on page 205.)

1. In what city was our first public high school established?
2. Who is considered the Father of the Kindergarten?
3. Where is the oldest university in the western hemisphere?
4. Why is graduation day called Commencement Day?
5. Which college does not have examinations?
6. What were dame schools?
7. When was Oxford University founded?
8. What is a co-operative college?
9. Is school attendance compulsory in all the States?
10. Whose writings have long formed the basis of education in China?
11. What and where is the Sorbonne?
12. Socrates used a special method of teaching, what was it?

13. Who was the most famous teacher of the 12th century?
14. What tests are widely used to test the intelligence of children?
15. Which university was endowed by George Washington?
16. Name a great Swiss educator of the past.
17. Define curriculum.
18. Which university has the largest enrollment?
19. Name three countries having the lowest percentage of illiteracy.
20. By whom were Rhodes Scholarships founded?
21. In which university was Thomas Jefferson especially interested?
22. For what is Charles W. Eliot noted besides being President of Harvard?
23. Who was Delsarte?
24. When did modern shorthand come in vogue?
25. Where is the United States Military Academy?

FINANCE QUIZ

Par for this Quiz is five minutes, but if you say so, we will be glad to declare a moratorium to enable you to meet your quizzical obligations. (Dividends will be found on page 206.)

1. What were the famous wheat corners?
2. Is par always 100?
3. Why is the curb market so called?
4. In English money, what is a bob?
5. Estimate the life of a dollar bill.
6. What system of coinage is used by most nations?
7. Give the proper name for an I.O.U.
8. In stock market language, what are cats and dogs?
9. How early were attempts made to corner a commodity?
10. When was the Rich Man's Panic?
11. With whom is the slogan 16 to 1 associated?
12. What was the first bank in the United States?
13. Who is said to have originated the gold standard?
14. Do long or short term bonds pay the higher return?

15. For what is Lombard Street famous? Where is it?
16. What is the name of the most famous banking family of Europe?
17. Is the Bank of England a government institution?
18. What famous street extends from Broadway to East River, New York?
19. Define moratorium.
20. Who was the great financier, recently dead, who was referred to as the mystery man?
21. Where is the bank for International Settlements?
22. In what country is the pengo used?
23. Which Secretary of the Treasury was the son-in-law of a President?
24. What great American financier is noted for his interest in art?
25. What term is used when, instead of paying a dividend, a stock is assessed requiring the owner to pay the corporation?

ETIQUETTE QUIZ

Should a lady assist a man in answering a Quiz? Is it proper to wear gloves and ear-muffs when quizzing your neighbor? (For the answers see page 207.)

1. In what person is a formal invitation written?
2. How long should a formal call last?
3. Is it correct to say, "Good morning Doctor?"
4. Is it in good taste to apply rouge and powder in public?
5. Upon the announcement of an engagement, who should be congratulated?
6. Name some of the so-called finger foods.
7. Who is credited with the introduction of finger bowls into this country?
8. Should a man walk between two women?
9. Is it correct to seal a letter of introduction?
10. Who is toastmaster at a wedding breakfast?
11. Should a lady assist a man in putting on his coat?
12. When dining out with a man does a woman give her order direct to the waiter?
13. Do good manners require one to leave some food on the plate?

14. Should one say please and thank you to servants?
15. When may a tuxedo be worn in daylight?
16. How long before a wedding should invitations be sent?
17. Is it good form to use Miss before one's name on calling cards?
18. If you are well acquainted with a man but do not know his wife, how do you address a Christmas card?
19. Should the wife of a physician refer to her husband as doctor?
20. If the president of a woman's organization is unmarried, do you address her as Miss President?
21. Does a boy in grade school have Mr. engraved on his cards?
22. May a clergyman be addressed as Reverend Brown?
23. How is a widow's card engraved?
24. Do members of a prospective bride's family give showers for her?
25. What do you do with gloves at a formal dinner, turn them back or remove them?

CURIOUS CUSTOMS QUIZ

In the old days they had a custom of "putting people to the question"—just a euphuism for torture. Perhaps you think the world hasn't changed much, after all! (See page 207 for the right answers.)

1. Why do we say goodbye?
2. Why are eggs used at Easter time?
3. The celebration of which great Christian festival owes its origin in part to the Roman Saturnalia?
4. Where did the wooden Indian as a tobacconist's sign originate?
5. The arms of what great Italian family are a well-known street sign today?
6. What is meant by "crossing the line"?
7. Where were Christmas celebrations forbidden in this country?
8. What is the kissing of the Blarney Stone supposed to confer?
9. Where did the custom of Eastern egg rolling begin?
10. Was scalping a purely Indian custom?
11. Why are imitation windows sometimes painted on barns?

12. How and when is Hogmanay celebrated?
13. What do totem poles stand for?
14. In what country did the custom of suttee prevail?
15. Whence came the fashion of wearing black crêpe for mourning?
16. To whom is credited the origin of leap year proposal?
17. Why were prison sentences given for a year and a day?
18. Who was the emperor who compiled a bulky code of etiquette known as the Book of Ceremonial?
19. Where do we get the name Santa Claus?
20. In what country do men as well as women carry fans?
21. What Queen popularized the wearing of silk stockings?
22. Why do Cardinals wear red hats?
23. What is an apostle spoon?
24. According to popular superstition, what should be part of the bridal costume?
25. When the Manchu conquered the Chinese, what mark of bondage were the latter forced to adopt?

ARMY AND NAVY QUIZ

Giving the wrong answer has led to more than one war, so watch your step! The right answers to this Quiz may be found on page 208.

1. Which is the largest army in the world?
2. Who names the U. S. Navy vessels?
3. Give the name for the tall fur hats worn by some English soldiers?
4. Who commanded our first regularly organized fleet?
5. How many divisions has the United States fleet? What are they?
6. Uhlans were conspicuous in what army?
7. What country has neither army nor navy?
8. At what age did Admiral Farragut enter the Navy?
9. Is a subaltern a commissioned officer or not?
10. Which French military decoration is most highly prized?
11. In a sailor's uniform for what do the thirteen buttons across the top of the trousers stand?
12. Why are midshipmen so called?
13. Do most countries have universal military service?

14. Name the 15 decisive battles of world history.

15. Which infantry corps is distinguished by a black drooping cock feather in their hats?

16. Who are the Devil Dogs, the Leathernecks?

17. Where is the headquarters of the French Foreign Legion?

18. Who said an army travels on its stomach?

19. What is the term applied to the maneuvering of troops on the field of battle?

20. When is Army Day?

21. For what are U. S. submarines named?

22. What branch of the Army uses the Caduceus as its insignia?

23. Who was in charge of our Navy during the World War?

24. Estimate the weight of a soldier's pack when fully equipped.

25. What term in the infantry corresponds to a troop of cavalry?

TRANSPORTATION QUIZ

*Transport comes from the Latin words trans (across) +
portare (to carry). Now this Quiz ought to be a cinch!
Just to make sure, however, you'd better carry over to page
209.*

1. What is the name given to a railroad or steamship
   company that carries passengers and goods for hire?
2. A wind-jammer is what kind of a ship?
3. What boat raced the *Robert E. Lee?* Which won?
4. How long does it take to go through the Panama
   Canal?
5. Who founded the Cunard Line?
6. What was Clinton's Folly?
7. How many locks are there in the Suez Canal?
8. Is more automobile traveling done on city streets or
   on country roads?
9. Why was a clipper ship so called?
10. Which canal carries the heaviest traffic?
11. Give the name for the line on a ship that shows how
    deeply she may be safely loaded.
12. Which was the longest Indian trail?

13. Estimate the number of miles the average automobile is driven in a year.
14. Which was the largest of the old clipper ships?
15. Where is the All-American Canal?
16. Which is the most-traveled highway in the United States?
17. For what Englishman is a common type of road named?
18. Where is the Going-to-the-Sun Highway?
19. How were railroad trains first described?
20. What were railroad conductors called a century ago?
21. Where and when was the first American railroad built?
22. What was the first locomotive to operate west of Chicago?
23. What railroad locomotive first had a whistle?
24. What were the first Pullman charges?
25. What was the date of the first dining car?

FLAG QUIZ

Here's a Quiz that will show your true colors! In case your spirits are flagging, just remember Barbara Frietche—or was it Betsy Ross? (Answers on page 210.)

1. Where is the flag that inspired the writing of the Star Spangled Banner?
2. Which star on the flag represents New York State?
3. Give four terms used for military flags.
4. May the United States Flag be used as a trademark?
5. Which was the first foreign salute to our flag?
6. Under how many flags has Texas existed?
7. There is only one flag that may be flown above the Stars and Stripes, what is it?
8. What is the birthday of the United States Flag?
9. Which flag consists of three crosses?
10. Which flag derives its name from the fact that it consists of three colors?
11. Which is the oldest flag in use today?
12. The flag of which foreign nation most nearly resembles our own?
13. Since when has our flag had forty-eight stars?

14. Which State has the Confederate battle flag as its state flag.
15. When should the flag be draped?
16. Name the only State having a coat-of-arms on its flag.
17. By what is a flagstaff topped?
18. Which flags have gold fringes?
19. By what name are flags on naval vessels generally known?
20. How is a flag correctly placed at half mast?
21. What do we call the light, woollen material from which flags are made?
22. For centuries red flags and black flags have had a special association, what is it?
23. Whose flag is charged with a rising sun?
24. What does the British flag symbolize?
25. Which flag is the Viercleur?

SLANG QUIZ

*Toe the mark, get a bee in your bonnet, cudgel your brains,
don't bark up the wrong tree, and never, never throw up
the sponge—and you'll be a Master Quizzer before you
know it. (Answers on page 210.)*

Define the following terms:

1. Axe to grind.
2. Throw up the sponge.
3. To call a spade a spade.
4. Crocodile tears.
5. Put in your oar.
6. Face the music.
7. Toe the mark.
8. Haul over the coals.
9. Break the ice.
10. Kick the bucket.
11. Let the cat out of the bag.
12. To go to Davy Jones' Locker.
13. Cudgel your brains.
14. Show the white feather.
15. So-so.

16. Paddle your own canoe.
17. Take the cake.
18. Black sheep.
19. Bee in your bonnet.
20. Throw dust in the eyes.
21. On tick.
22. Wild goose chase.
23. Blow hot and cold.
24. Born with a silver spoon in one's mouth.
25. Barking up the wrong tree.

AMERICANA QUIZ

"America," says Emerson, "is another name for opportunity." So, here's your opportunity to make a perfect score! (For the correct answers, see page 211.)

1. From what point in the United States could one look due south into Canada?
2. When and by whom did the United States get its present name?
3. Which of our dependencies are territories?
4. Which State joined the Union with the understanding that it might later subdivide?
5. May rural mail boxes be painted in color?
6. Which is further west, Reno, Nevada, or Los Angeles, California?
7. Has this country a national tree?
8. Which State is most densely populated in proportion to its size?
9. Are there any town criers nowadays?
10. Who was nicknamed the Kingfish?
11. Identify the famous building designed by an Irishman, James Hoban.
12. Are whipping posts still in use as a form of punishment?

[93]

13. Fine horses, lovely women, good whiskey are associated with what State?

14. Who were the Wide-awakes?

15. Who first said, "the mails must go through"?

16. Name the most easterly possession of the United States.

17. How many men have served as President of the United States?

18. Who was the bachelor President?

19. Which President had fourteen children?

20. Who was the youngest President to assume office?

21. Which President died after one month in office?

22. What was a bounty jumper in the Civil War?

23. On what date was Franklin D. Roosevelt inaugurated the second time?

24. Who was the only President re-elected after a defeat?

25. Which President went through his term without a change in his cabinet?

FIRST THINGS QUIZ

While we are on the subject of first things, the first Quiz took place in the Garden of Eden, when the Lord asked Adam and Eve: "Who told thee that thou wast naked? Hast thou eaten of the tree?" (Answers to this Quiz are on page 211.)

1. Where were the first bricks made in America?
2. Name the first daily newspaper in the United States?
3. The first motion picture theatre was opened in which city?
4. Who first suggested daylight saving?
5. The honor of being the first skyscraper goes to what building?
6. By what ship was the American flag first carried around the world?
7. For what was Mergenthaler noted?
8. By whom was the first air-brake made?
9. Who was the first Vice-President of the United States?
10. When was the United States flag first fired upon during the Civil War?
11. Why was the steamer *Walk-in-the-Water* noted?

12. Who was the first white child born on American soil?
13. Who discovered aluminum?
14. In which city was the first theatre in this country established?
15. The words, "What hath God wrought," are famous for what reason?
16. What was the first educational endowment in America?
17. Who was known as the First Gentleman of Europe?
18. Name the first woman cabinet member in the United States.
19. When was glass first manufactured?
20. Name the first President of France.
21. Who was Woodrow Wilson's first wife?
22. What woman made the first trip around the world?
23. By whom was the doctrine of the Freedom of the Seas first propounded?
24. Who made the first cotton gin?
25. What happened in Eldorado County, California, in 1848?

FOODS QUIZ

You will find plenty of food for thought in these twenty-five questions. The correct answers may be found on page 212.

1. Name four kinds of lilies used for food.
2. Is rice grown in the United States?
3. Of what does a cake of yeast consist?
4. Is it correct to say cole slaw or cold slaw?
5. How did Porterhouse steak get its name?
6. What food adds lime to the body?
7. What is the most widely used foodstuff in the world?
8. How long does it take food to go from the mouth to the stomach?
9. In what country are birds' nests an article of food?
10. What are sweetbreads?
11. Name the British peer who gave his name to a popular article of food.
12. To which country is coffee indigenous?
13. Is the peanut a nut?
14. Which foods are richest in iodine?
15. How many pounds are there in a barrel of flour?
16. What kind of gourds are edible?

[97]

17. What kind of steak is cooked on a special wooden platter with a groove?
18. The staff of life refers to what daily food?
19. What are the brain foods?
20. What is the most complete single food?
21. For which king of England is a popular American dish named? What is it?
22. Red caviar is made by what fish roe?
23. What gives Worcestershire sauce its characteristic flavor?
24. What food do we get from the trunk of a palm tree?
25. By what Government Department are food tasters employed?

FOREIGN WORDS AND PHRASES QUIZ

If you are non compos mentis, never cry Eureka until your Quiz is a fait accompli. And, even then, it might be wise to look at page 212.

What is the meaning of:

1. Homo sapiens.
2. Te Deum laudamus.
3. Maître d'hôtel.
4. Pro rata.
5. Non compos mentis.
6. Ich dien.
7. Tête-à-tête.
8. Ex libris.
9. Enfant terrible.
10. Casus belli.
11. Weldschmertz.
12. Banzai.
13. Querido amigo mio.
14. Noblesse oblige.
15. Lèse majesté.

16. Mirabile dictu.
17. Locum tenens.
18. De mortuis nil nisi bonum.
19. Wanderlust.
20. Quien sabe?
21. Swaraj.
22. Dies irae.
23. Jeunesse dorée.
24. Eureka.
25. Guadeamus igitur.

SUPERSTITIONS QUIZ

Did you put your right shoe on first when you dressed this morning? If you did, then you should have good luck with this Quiz. Don't be superstitious about looking on page 213 for the right answers.

1. Why is it unlucky to spill salt?
2. Why is a cat said to have nine lives?
3. What do you carry to bring good luck?
4. Whence do we get the belief regarding the lighting of three cigarettes from one match?
5. In rehearsing a play, which line must not be spoken?
6. What animal was said to fascinate by its look?
7. Will a horsehair thrown into a pool change into a snake?
8. How should a horseshoe be hung to bring good luck?
9. What is ascending smoke supposed to indicate?
10. Which jewel is considered unlucky?
11. In what country are houses constructed with odd numbers of floors and steps to ensure good luck?
12. Why is the four-leaved clover considered lucky?
13. "Rainbow at night, shepherd's delight, . . ." complete the saying.

14. Is a banshee supposed to be a man or a woman?

15. What superstition is connected with the Fountain of Trevi in Rome?

16. A red sun has what?

17. Is sleeping in a north and south position preferable to any other?

18. Does the moon effect people either mentally or physically?

19. What is the superstition connected with being born with a caul or veil?

20. What is one of the superstitions regarding the cure for convulsions?

21. In putting on the shoes which should go on first to bring good luck?

22. According to superstition which day of the week is best for a wedding?

23. What is the origin of the superstition that it is unlucky to break a mirror?

24. Some countries believe stones grow. Is this possible?

25. Why do Indians decorate their costumes with feathers?

ADVERTISING SLOGANS QUIZ

This Quiz will show up the chap who boasts: "I buy the Post only to look at the ads." The correct answers are to be found on page 214.

1. "All the News that's fit to print" will be found where?
2. What watch is advertised as "the watch of railroad accuracy"?
3. "Ivory Tips Protect" whose lips?
4. Who says that "Life Begins at 40"?
5. When do you "Sleep Like a Kitten"?
6. To what should you devote Fifteen Minutes a Day?
7. Who warns you of the "Danger Line"?
8. What is "Good to the Last Drop"?
9. Addison Sims of Seattle reminded you of what?
10. "They are the largest selling cigarette in America" is used in reference to which cigarettes?
11. "It Never Rains but it Pours," say the makers of what product?
12. What is "Dated"?
13. Who tells you to "Ask the Man Who Owns One"?
14. What piano is said to be the "Instrument of the Immortals"?

15. Who gives us "Milk from Contented Cows"?
16. What "Covers the Earth"?
17. Who says "It's Time to Retire"?
18. "Do as Your Dentist Does" with what?
19. Children Cry for what?
20. What "Hasn't Scratched Yet"?
21. How do you "Keep that School Girl Complexion"?
22. What keeps away B. O.?
23. "Eventually, Why Not Now," refers to what?
24. Who warns against "Tattletale Gray"?
25. What has "Made Milwaukee Famous"?

SHIPS AND NAVIGATION QUIZ

Rough going ahead! Port your helm and polish up your binnacle, and the less barnacles on your bilge the better score you will make in this naughty nautical test. Look in the stern sheets, page 214, for the answers.

1. What were the names of Christopher Columbus' three ships?
2. What vessel was the first ship to use steam in crossing an ocean?
3. What was the name of the first Cunard liner?
4. What has become of the *Leviathan?*
5. What are the names of the two largest passenger liners now afloat?
6. Who was Nathaniel Bowditch?
7. What is the collective noun used to refer to employees on a ship?
8. What passenger vessel burned off the New Jersey coast in September, 1934?
9. How fast do American freighters travel?
10. What Canadian vessel was sunk by the Coast Guard off Louisiana in 1929?
11. What is a sextant?

12. In what year did the famous race between the *Natchez* and the *Robert E. Lee* occur?

13. Where is *Old Ironsides?*

14. What was the German name of the *Leviathan?*

15. What is the name of a large company which insures ocean vessels?

16. What are the three classes of accommodations for passengers on ocean liners?

17. What is a cargo vessel which has no fixed itinerary called?

18. What was the name of the largest sail vessel ever built in the United States?

19. Was the *Titanic* ever salvaged?

20. What United States vessel was destroyed in the harbor of Havana in 1898?

21. What two ships took part in a famous battle at Hampton Roads during the Civil War?

22. What was the name of the yacht used by the four Presidents preceding Hoover?

23. By what famous Admiral was the flagship *Hartford* used?

24. How many mutinies have occurred on United States Naval vessels?

25. What is the record of a ship's cruise called?

RELIGION QUIZ

Will Carleton once said: "To appreciate heaven well 'tis good for a man to have some fifteen minutes of hell." So go to it! For the right answers, look back in the vestry, on page 215.

1. What is meant by the tree of Jesse?
2. Who was the sweet singer of Israel?
3. Which is the largest and costliest Protestant church in New York City?
4. Name the five principal virtues urged by Confucius?
5. When was Sad Palm Sunday?
6. What is the term of office of a Cardinal?
7. Give another name of Buchmanism.
8. What was a sin eater?
9. Who was the Wise or Enlightened one?
10. Explain the difference between Agnosticism and Atheism.
11. What god is represented with four heads and four arms?
12. Who was the greatest modern Jewish historian?
13. Shintoism is the religion of what country?

14. Did John and Charles Wesley visit America?
15. Who began the Protestant Reformation?
16. Define Catholic.
17. What religion was founded by a woman?
18. What is the Talmud?
19. Give the popular name for the Society of Friends.
20. To what does Muezzin refer?
21. What is a monotheistic religion?
22. To what does the anxious bench, or anxious seat refer?
23. What were the Wars of Religion?
24. The flight of Mohammed from Mecca to Medina is known by what term?
25. By what name is the shaven part of a monk's head known?

COIN QUIZ

Heads you win, tails you lose! But don't leave it all to the toss of a coin. Turn back to page 215 for the bona fide answers.

1. Which is the parent mint in the United States?
2. Is obverse the front or back of a coin?
3. Where did coins originate?
4. What country issued red and white porcelain coins during the World War?
5. What name is given to a book giving the moneys of different countries and their equivalents?
6. In what country is the guinea used? What is its value?
7. What is meant by debasing coinage?
8. Why do coins have milled edges?
9. What do the letters "d" and "s" mean on some coins?
10. In what country is the rupee used?
11. What was a slave coin?
12. In speaking of tax levies the term mill is used. Is there such a coin?
13. How long has the head of Liberty been used on American coins?

14. Is stone money actually in use anywhere in the world?

15. By what general term are coins and metallic money known?

16. How many Confederate half-dollars were struck?

17. What nation at one time made their coins in the shape of the things they wanted to buy?

18. With what are our gold and silver coins alloyed?

19. The scalp of what bird was at one time used as money in America?

20. About when did the motto, "In God we Trust," first appear on our coins?

21. What determines the value of a coin, its age or rarity and condition?

22. Of which country is the zloti the monetary unit?

23. What is bullion?

24. What is a simple way of telling a copper coin from a brass coin?

25. Were there ever any coins bearing the figure of an angel?

STAMP QUIZ

Almost anybody would be glad to become a philatelist if the word still meant what it did in the old Greek days. (See page 216 for the answers to this Quiz.)

1. Has a President of the United States been honored by a foreign stamp issue?
2. For what purpose are duck stamps sold?
3. Which country issued a stamp depicting Mount Ararat where Noah's Ark is said to have rested?
4. What is an Albino Stamp?
5. Do any stamps picture Jesus Christ?
6. Stamp collecting has been the hobby of two important modern rulers, who are they?
7. Which author of an international language has been honored by a stamp?
8. What does the word philately mean literally?
9. Name the stamp of which only one specimen exists.
10. What is meant by cover?
11. For what does Svalbard on a stamp stand?
12. Whose picture did the first real stamps issued by this country bear?
13. By what means was mail carried to the West in the early days?

14. What country issued the first postage stamp?
15. By what name is a stamp collector known?
16. What are demonetized stamps?
17. Define "avion" found on some stamps.
18. Where are letters sent when addressee and sender cannot be found?
19. For what do the letters B.C.M. stand?
20. What country issued a grasshopper stamp and why?
21. Who originated the idea of the postage stamp?
22. What do the letters T.E.O. and O.M.F. mean when overprinted on some French stamps?
23. What are Queen's Heads?
24. Where is Tannou Touva?
25. Who makes our postage stamps?

GENEALOGY QUIZ

It is fine to have had a sixteen carat family pedigree, but when you face a Quiz a dolphin on your coat-of-arms or a heraldic knot wont make these questions any the less knotty. (The right answers are on page 217.)

1. Do the genealogical lines traced in the Old Testament indicate the descent of families?
2. Do many family pedigrees run back to Roman times?
3. Has the business of searching genealogies long been practiced?
4. During the crusades the French soldiers attached their national emblem fleur-de-lys to the ends of the members of the Cross. By what name is this device now known?
5. Are mottoes granted by the Herald's College?
6. What is a quartered shield?
7. How did the crest originate?
8. How are gold or yellow termed and indicated in heraldry?
9. A coat-of-arms, fully emblazoned, is known by what term?
10. What is regarded as surest proof of pedigree?

11. Are old English and Welsh parish records considered trustworthy in matters of genealogy?

12. Why was the Dauphin of France so called?

13. Do old Irish families have coats-of-arms?

14. Do the designs on coats-of-arms have any significance related to the name or family?

15. Were coats-of-arms in use at the time of the Norman Conquest?

16. What is a crest in heraldry?

17. What is a difference in heraldry?

18. What is the difference between a coat-of-arms and a badge?

19. What is a marshalled coat-of-arms?

20. Are there any blank coats-of-arms?

21. Does the bend sinister in heraldry denote illegitimacy?

22. Name the first English sovereign to appear on his great seal with arms on his shield.

23. In what country is there a Lyon King of Arms?

24. Who is the Earl Marshal of England?

25. What is meant by visitation in heraldry?

EXPLORATION QUIZ

The poet Gray wrote: "Some bold adventurers disdain the limits of their little reign, and unknown regions dare descry." So, cast off, and see how good you are at finding the right answers. (See page 218.)

1. Whose ship was named the *Golden Hind?*
2. Who was the American President famed for his exploring trips?
3. What explorer gave his name for a camera?
4. Locate Little America.
5. Dr. Beebe used a special device in exploring the ocean depths, what was it?
6. Who received the Congressional Medal of Honor on his 91st birthday for Arctic exploration?
7. Name four noted women explorers.
8. Did Magellan round Cape Horn?
9. What explorer took cows with him on a polar trip?
10. With whom is the legend of Rip Van Winkle connected?
11. Where is the Explorers' Club?
12. How did Amundsen meet his death?
13. Has the submarine ever been used in polar exploration?

14. By whom was the Mississippi River discovered?

15. For what was Ponce de Leon searching?

16. The Great Age of Discovery refers to what period?

17. Who is the best known colored explorer?

18. Who explored Australia and was killed by natives in the Hawaiian Islands?

19. Name the great traveller of the Middle Ages who spent seventeen years in China.

20. What explorer succeeded in reaching the North Pole after seven attempts?

21. Diaries of an explorer lost for many years were discovered in 1930. Who was he?

22. Who first carried the British flag around the world?

23. What was sought by many explorers of the north?

24. Who is the Glacier Priest noted for his exploration of Alaska?

25. Name the special food, of American Indian origin, that is favored by explorers.

HEALTH QUIZ

The average blood pressure varies between 90 and 150 mm, but wait until you start working on the Quiz below! We're warning you in advance. (Correct answers on page 218.)

1. State the average normal temperature of the human body.
2. How long does it take the blood to circulate through the body?
3. Who was the Father of Medicine?
4. What is composed of carbon, hydrogen, oxygen, nitrogen, sulphur, phosphorus?
5. How many bones are there in the arm?
6. What term is used for the classification of diseases?
7. Explain the difference between ganglion and gangrene.
8. Who was missionary to the lepers in Hawaii?
9. What disease is transmitted by a louse?
10. Does the hair grow after death?
11. What is the name of the organism which causes the common cold?
12. Give the word used to mean (1) sensitivity to substances; (2) power to do work.

13. What does eugenics mean literally?
14. How is bubonic plague transmitted?
15. Is a person taller when lying down or when standing up?
16. Is a single corpuscle of blood red?
17. Estimate as nearly as possible the number of square inches of skin of the average adult.
18. At what age should the body weight reach its highest?
19. Name the largest bone in the body.
20. How many teeth are there in the baby set?   In the adult set?
21. What is popularly termed the third lung?
22. Give the name for the groove extending from the upper lip to the nose.
23. What is the organ of speech?
24. Where is the solar plexus located?
25. What disease killed more American soldiers than were killed in battle?

FAMILIAR POEMS QUIZ

Many of us have been accused of "being a poet who doesn't know it." Here is a good chance to show how good our poetic memories are. (Correct answers on page 219.)

1. Complete the lines: *"Count that day lost whose low descending sun........"*
2. What is the name of the poem beginning, *"Grow old along with me"?*
3. Complete, . . . *"I have a little shadow that goes in and out with me".........*
4. Complete, . . . *"Lo the poor Indian whose untutored mind".......*
5. Who wrote the lines, *"When God sorts out the weather and sends rain, why rain's my choice"?*
6. Give the first line of, "America for Me," by Henry Van Dyke.
7. Finish the lines, . . . *"My candle burns at both ends".......*
8. Identify the poem which begins, *"Over the river and through the wood to grandfather's house we go."*
9. Who wrote the verses ending: *"The everlastin' teamwork of every bloomin' soul"?*

10. What famous writer popularized the lines, *"You are Old Father William"*?

11. Give the next line after *"The world is so full of a number of things."*

12. Who wrote the "Blessed Damozel"?

13. Give the source of the following, *"Water, water everywhere."*

14. *" 'Tis better to have loved and lost,"* Than........ what?

15. By whom was the "Ode to a Grecian Urn" written?

16. *"A loaf of bread, a jug of wine and thou"*—from what poem do we get this?

17. Complete *"Stone walls do not a prison make"*—

18. In whose memory did Tennyson write "In Memoriam"?

19. What is the name of the poem beginning, *"A fool there was and he made his prayer, even as you and I"*?

20. Complete the line, *"Oh, East is East and West is West, and"*.........

21. *"Stay, stay at home my heart and rest........"* is from a poem by whom?

22. "The Vision of Sir Launfal" is by Lowell, Longfellow or Riley?

23. Complete the following: *"There is no flock however watched and tended but"*.........

24. *"All the world's a stage and all the men and women merely players,"*—is from what play?

25. Complete the verse: *"Gather ye rosebuds while ye may, Old Time is still"*.........

FAMILIAR SONGS QUIZ

Someone once said: "A song will outlive all sermons in the memory." See how good your memory is when it comes to these old favorites. (Correct answers on page 219.)

1. When you hear "The Sidewalks of New York," do you think of President Roosevelt, Jimmy Walker or Al Smith?

2. "Old Man River" recalls the famous musical production entitled: "Of Thee I sing," "The Merry Widow," or "Show Boat"?

3. What is the name of the old song beginning, *"I wandered today to the hill, Maggie"?*

4. What composer wrote the song beginning, *"O, Susanna! O, don't you cry for me"?*

5. What song about Kentucky contains the line, *"The time has come when the darkies have to part"?*

6. From what show is the song, "Easter Parade"?

7. "Alexander's Ragtime Band" is a song composed by which one of the following: George Gershwin, Irving Berlin, Nacio Herb Brown?"

8. What noted composer wrote "Rhapsody in Blue"?

9. *"Reading and writing and 'rithmetic taught to the tune of a hickory stick,"* is a line from what song?

10. *"Wynken, Blynken, and Nod one night sailed off,"* how?

11. *"The hours I spent with thee, dear heart,"* are as what?

12. *"Who wept with delight when you gave her a smile—?*

13. The line *"Way down upon the Swanee River"* is from what famous song?

14. Who wrote the words of the "Battle Hymn of the Republic"?

15. What American and British patriotic songs are sung to the same tune?

16. Give the first line of the chorus of "The Quilting Party."

17. What kind of song is "Deep River"?

18. What line follows, *"Darling, I am growing old."*

19. What was the popular French song of the World War?

20. What famous sextette begins with the words, *"Tell me pretty maiden, are there any more at home like you"?*

21. Name the famous war song written by George M. Cohan.

22. Give the next line after: *"Should auld aquaintance be forgot........."*

23. In the song, "Comin' Through the Rye," to what does Rye refer?

24. Give the name of the popular song written by Queen Liliuokalani of Hawaii?

25. What song often sung at weddings was interpolated in the score of "Robin Hood"?

JUNIOR QUIZ NUMBER 1

These questions are for Junior, but there is no law against Father or Mother trying their skill at answering all twenty-five correctly. The correct answers are on page 220.

1. What does a bee get from a flower?
2. Of what country is St. Patrick the patron saint?
3. Is it easier to swim in fresh or in salt water?
4. How many sides has a triangle?
5. Who wrote "Treasure Island"?
6. What instrument measures heat?
7. The British Isles include what countries?
8. Whose life did Pocahontas save?
9. For what do the letters B.C. and A.D. stand?
10. Where did the Northmen come from?
11. Is Monday the first day of the week?
12. Where do we get silk from?
13. What is the difference between a papoose and a porpoise?
14. How many notes are there in the musical scale?
15. For whom was Pennsylvania named?
16. What birds carry messages?
17. Who is famous for his home runs?

18. What European country is shaped like a boot?
19. What is the Big Dipper?
20. Who makes our laws?
21. What color denotes danger?
22. Is data singular or plural?
23. By what nickname was William Frederick Cody known?
24. With what do you connect the Wright Brothers?
25. Name the time zones in the United States.

JUNIOR QUIZ NUMBER 2

The person who made up Question Number nine ought to be shot for asking it in a Junior Quiz! When you've answered all of the questions, turn to page 220 to see whether you are right or wrong.

1. Who discovered the Pacific Ocean?
2. Where is the tallest building in the world?
3. For what does R.F.D. stand?
4. Who said, "Give me•liberty or give me death?"
5. Name the island on which the Statue of Liberty stands?
6. Who wrote the "Stars and Stripes Forever?"
7. What country is noted for its windmills?
8. Explain the difference between apiary and aviary.
9. What well-known medicine comes from a bean?
10. Name the capital city of Sweden, Brazil, Australia.
11. Who is the Vice-President of the United States?
12. What implement is used to capture whales?
13. A fertile spot in the desert is called by what name?
14. Who is author of "Just-So Stories"?
15. Cuba is the largest island of what group?

16. What is a young swan called?
17. The children of what town were charmed by the Pied Piper?
18. What two States were admitted to the Union at the same time?
19. Who was Captain Kidd?
20. What common bird lays blue eggs?
21. Which of Jesus' Disciples denied Him?
22. In what city is the Liberty Bell?
23. Which star guides mariners?
24. Identify the following as to profession: Napoleon, Alexander Graham Bell, Handel, Mark Twain.
25. What is the name of an Eskimo hut?

BRAIN TEASER QUIZ

Did you know that a frog has teeth? You will find that some of these Brain Teasers have teeth in them, too. (For the correct answers, see page 221.)

1. In what kingdom is the greatest oxygen factory in the world?
2. What paved road ran from Rome south through Capua to Brindisi?
3. It has been said that free-wheeling has been used on a common household machine for many years, what is it?
4. What is remarkable about the Kryailteyo Pagoda in Burma?
5. Give the name of the famous short story in which a husband pawns his watch to buy combs for his wife, who had sold her hair to buy him a fob.
6. Why do artists prefer a north light?
7. Can you finish Swift's doggerel: "So, naturalists observe, a flea has smaller fleas that on him prey; ...."
8. Is there a limit beyond which nothing can be colder?
9. Who really wrote the "Letters of Junius?"

10. What was the most extensive empire ever established?

11. What precious stone was by the ancients thought to be an antidote to inebriation?

12. How did Joshua cause the Walls of Jericho to fall?

13. Give the name and location of the highest mountain ever climbed by man.

14. A woolsack is the seat of what important personage?

15. How many eggs does a cod fish lay?

16. What is the meaning of Shangri-La, referred to in "Lost Horizon"?

17. What is a characteristic difference between a frog and a toad?

18. How many numbers are represented in abracadabra?

19. In what town is the Street of the Ouled Naïls?

20. Is it possible for a violin note to break a glass?

21. Does a person rise to the surface three times before drowning?

22. What is white coal?

23. Is a cyclone an area of high pressure or low pressure?

24. What is topiary work?

25. Who went in search of the Golden Fleece?

SUPER QUIZ NUMBER 1

This one is for college professors and a few trombone players! You have to have a high I.Q. and low blood pressure and you're sunk if you have water on the brain! Even Prof. Quiz had to keep his finger on page 221.

1. Where is the Beaufort Sea?
2. On what division of time is the Jewish calendar based?
3. Which is the smallest flowering plant? How large is it?
4. What are girandoles?
5. Which king stood on a stool when he was crowned?
6. Who is Pertinax?
7. What poem was said by Lord Byron to be the most perfect in the English language?
8. Is there a point where four States touch?
9. Give the six fundamental principles of the Constitution.
10. What organ controls the sense of balance in the body?
11. Is there a wingless bird?
12. How hard must the wind blow to be called a hurricane?

13. What prevents the making of 100 per cent efficient machines?

14. Name the wife of Socrates.

15. Define levirate marriage.

16. What is a clerestory?

17. From what poem is the line, "I have been faithful to thee Cynara! in my fashion"?

18. Identify, "Tod und Verklärung."

19. Give the scientific term for split personality.

20. What and where are Scylla and Charybdis?

21. In what city did the Medici family flourish?

22. For what does S.P.Q.R. stand?

23. In which constellation is the sun?

24. How much does crime cost the United States annually?

25. What is popularly spoken of as the most northerly point of Great Britain?

SUPER QUIZ NUMBER 2

*Pago-Pago is pronounced Pango-Pango, but where is it?
When you have answered that we'll ask you to answer
Samoa! (See page 222 for correct Quiz answers.)*

1. From what did Hogarth derive his famous line of beauty?
2. Give the inscription found on Buddhist prayer-wheels.
3. What is the name for the gateway of a Shinto Temple?
4. Name two great places of amusement in ancient Rome.
5. Soviet Russia dominates what Far Eastern State that is nominally a part of China?
6. What are the chances of winning in the numbers game?
7. What game, popular in America, symbolized the Great Wall of China?
8. Name the oldest breed of dog.
9. What was known as the solar plexus bout?
10. What famous discovery was made by observing a frog's legs?
11. Where is Pago-Pago?

12. Who was the newspaper correspondent who won the Pulitzer Prize for his interview with President Roosevelt?

13. A great Attic orator as a boy had an impediment in his speech, who was he?

14. What great German composer married the daughter of a world-famous pianist?

15. What "patient insect" taught Robert Bruce a lesson?

16. Give the opening statement of Caesar's Commentaries.

17. What is the costliest metal?

18. In what country is red hair most common?

19. Who is credited with the greatest musical memory of all time?

20. To whom was the Theatre of Dionysius in Athens dedicated?

21. Give the popular and literal translation of Sayonara.

22. What is the source of the expression, *"Closer is He than breathing And nearer than hands and feet?"*

23. Who was known as Old Probabilities?

24. Where is the tomb of Ferdinand and Isabella?

25. What is a nixie?

MISCELLANEOUS QUIZ NUMBER 1

Here is a pot-pourri for Mr. and Mrs. Average Citizen. All you need is a little SAVOIR FAIRE, and you will get a good mark. (Answers on page 223.)

1. What ancient city was saved by the cackling of geese?
2. Who solved the riddle of the Sphinx?
3. To what does Old Lady of Threadneedle Street refer?
4. What is a termagant?
5. Define Gestapo.
6. Give the national emblem of Scotland, France, Egypt, Spain.
7. What was President Wilson's first name?
8. By whom was the Koran written?
9. Where is the iron pillar that never rusts though exposed to the atmosphere?
10. Which is the oldest existing republic?
11. What city was known as the Bride of the Sea?
12. Is there such a country as Montenegro?
13. Who are the Untouchables?
14. Whose wife had to be above suspicion?

15. Who were Willy and Nicky in the Willy-Nicky Correspondence?
16. Where is the Iberian Peninsula?
17. To what does polyandry refer?
18. Where did Huckleberry Finn's adventures take place?
19. What is meant by "savoir faire?"
20. Who cleaned the Augean Stables?
21. Whence do we get the line, "A thing of beauty is a joy forever"?
22. Where did the slogan originate?
23. For what is a marlinspike used?
24. Who invented spectacles?
25. For what was Madame Tussaud famous?

MISCELLANEOUS QUIZ NUMBER 2

Do London cops carry copra through the coppice? That sounds a bit mixed up, but what can you expect in a Miscellaneous Quiz? (Answers on page 223.)

1. Should the word suit or suite be applied to a set of furniture?
2. Do London police carry guns?
3. What tragic event occurred in 1912?
4. Name the three principal islands of New Zealand.
5. Why is the passion flower so named?
6. Who was the only woman judge of Israel?
7. What are the "Vailima Letters"?
8. How much wax is there in sealing wax?
9. What saint lived on top of a pillar?
10. For what does A.A.U. stand?
11. Was there a real person named Robin Hood?
12. Where is the famous cathedral clock that indicates holidays and religious festivals?
13. Do orchids grow from seed?
14. From what animal do we get nutria fur?
15. What famous foreigner was given citizenship in Maryland in reward for his services to this country?

16. What two seas are joined by the Suez Canal?
17. For what is copra used?
18. Which aquatic bird does not fly?
19. For what is Belleek noted?
20. What does Bimetallism imply?
21. For what were Diaghileff, Mordkin, Nijinski noted?
22. Who was the slave who wrote a book of fables?
23. Whose was the face that launched a thousand ships?
24. How many acres in a square mile?
25. What South American capital is named Vale of Paradise?

MISCELLANEOUS QUIZ NUMBER 3

You may know where the Bodleian Library is, but it's too far away to be of much help in solving Miscellaneous Quiz Number 3. (See page 224 for the right answers.)

1. Does a hen sit or set on an egg?
2. Who was the Man of Destiny?
3. What Senator began his career as a newsboy?
4. What two signers of the Constitution became Presidents?
5. Why is a bus boy so-called?
6. Which is the largest artery in the body?
7. What is bagasse?
8. Who was the "Scourge of God"?
9. What was Samuel Johnson's favorite beverage?
10. For what was ancient Delphi famous?
11. Who was Sancho Panza?
12. What city of note is on the Whangpoo River?
13. Translate, Il Duce.
14. A cenotaph is what type of memorial?
15. How much lead is there in a lead pencil?
16. What and where is the "Spirit of St. Louis"?
17. When is Corpus Christi?

18. For what is Cremona, Italy, famous?
19. How many sheets of paper are there in a quire?
20. Who wrote "Lead Kindly Light"?
21. The opposite of zenith is what?
22. To what does lacrimae Christi refer?
23. Where is the Bodleian Library?
24. What is the port of Jerusalem?
25. Who was the Good Gray Poet?

MISCELLANEOUS QUIZ NUMBER 4

To the person who is "behind the 8-ball,"—and aren't we all?—it is small comfort to know that the expression came from the game of —— (the answer to Question 23 will be found on page 224.)

1. From what animal do we obtain the most expensive wool?
2. How many days were omitted when the new style calendar was adopted?
3. How many States are named for Presidents?
4. For whom was the Reo automobile named?
5. What is rice paper made of?
6. Who was the French Aesop?
7. What position in baseball did Pop Anson play?
8. Name the one common flower that produces true yellow, blue and red blossoms in the same species.
9. Give another name for encephalitis.
10. Define hoi polloi?
11. What element is found in all acids?
12. Where is the Battle of Flowers celebrated?
13. For what do the following stand: FDIC, SEC, FCC?

14. Which country is current in its payment on the World War debt?

15. Who was thus described, *"Age cannot wither her, nor custom stale her infinite variety"?*

16. What is meant by dying in the odor of sanctity?

17. Give the German phrase for "Until we meet again"?

18. What is the literal meaning of Sinn Fein?

19. In Colonial Days what was an ordinary?

20. What is the difference between a rebellion and a revolution?

21. Which is the smallest planet?

22. Are the Philippines completely independent?

23. Whence do we get the expression, "Behind the 8-ball"?

24. What is a Barmecide feast?

25. Which opera deals with a band of traveling mountebanks?

MISCELLANEOUS QUIZ NUMBER 5

There can be K------rs in other games besides cards. The Quizibitzer is someone you want to stay away from. He will tell you the answers before you can look back to page 225.

1. Where is the Giant's Causeway?
2. For what does G. R. stand in connection with the King of England?
3. Which fur is most difficult to imitate?
4. Which is the largest glacier in Switzerland?
5. Why is blue so often used with Sheraton furniture?
6. In what language do the post offices of the world communicate?
7. Who in 1905 hired a special train which made a record run between Los Angeles and Chicago?
8. When one person calls another on the telephone, who should say goodbye first?
9. Who were the three friends referred to in Longfellow's sonnet, "Three Friends of Mine"?
10. How did grog receive its name?
11. Who is one who takes no part in a card game but gives unasked advice?

12. What ancient people were famous for their stoicism and endurance?
13. Who were Guiteau, Czolgosz and Booth?
14. For what do the letters G.M.T. stand?
15. What is the greatest solvent?
16. Name the country having the largest area.
17. Which has greater influence upon tide, the sun or moon? Why?
18. Who is the hero of the Odyssey?
19. What does a red silk star on a postman's uniform mean?
20. Who wrote "Of Human Bondage"?
21. Who was George Romney?
22. Where is Roosevelt Dam?
23. When did the Battle of Little Big Horn take place?
24. What Indian chief was responsible for the Custer Massacre?
25. Give the meaning of the word stet.

MISCELLANEOUS QUIZ NUMBER 6

This one is easy. All except Question Number 17, which is a horse on us! Answers to Miscellaneous Quiz Number 6 are on page 226.

1. What teams competed in the first World Series?
2. Which inland body of water has the greatest percentage of salt?
3. What is the motto on the New Supreme Court Building?
4. How many voyages did Columbus make?
5. From what source did Hutchinson get the title of his book "If Winter Comes"?
6. Which British Sovereign had the longest reign?
7. To what family does the Christmas rose belong?
8. Who is the author of "The Man Who Married a Dumb Wife"?
9. What organization uses the motto, "Certainty, Security, Celerity"?
10. Which State capitol has forty-eight steps, each inscribed with the name of a State in the Union?
11. Who started the custom of saying hello over the telephone?

12. What do the letters V.A.D. stand for?
13. Why were the Cinque Ports so-called?
14. Name the first aeroplane to fly over the North Pole.
15. Which actor was noted for his role of Rip Van Winkle?
16. Give the plural of genius, crisis, stimulus.
17. For what is the hand a unit of measurement?
18. Chequers is the name of whose country home?
19. What occasioned the creation of the cartoon of the teddy bear?
20. Which Emperor fiddled while Rome burned?
21. Who made the "Cross of Gold" speech?
22. Where is Napoleon buried?
23. Who drank the fatal cup of hemlock?
24. By what term are the administrative divisions of Switzerland called?
25. What city has just completed two remarkable bridges?

MISCELLANEOUS QUIZ NUMBER 7

You ought to be able to answer all of the questions in this Quiz in six minutes, with enough time left over to look back to page 226 to check your answers.

1. What do newspaper men mean by masthead?
2. Who represented the United States in the Louisiana Purchase?
3. What company uses the largest amount of newspaper advertising?
4. Could a woman serve as President of the United States?
5. Do the Dunkards prohibit telephones and radios?
6. Who was the first martyr to the Christian faith?
7. Where is the late Senator Huey Long buried?
8. Are Christmas seals confined to the United States?
9. What was the Spanish Fury?
10. How much of the land surface of the United States is desert?
11. Who divided the ages of man into seven?
12. What kind of wood is used for fine cigar boxes?
13. How many cocoons does it take to make a pair of silk stockings?

14. In whose memory is the new stadium near Colorado Springs, Colorado?

15. Name the baseball player who first pitched a perfect game.

16. How many knights sat at King Arthur's Round Table.

17. Where in Europe is the Iron Gate?

18. Which of Columbus' ships was the largest?

19. Give the name of the lake at Boulder Dam.

20. Is there a university in this country that has no students and no faculty?

21. By whom was the first lightning rod devised?

22. To what does Cliveden refer?

23. Who succeeded Jane Addams as head of Hull House in Chicago?

24. Which State has the largest number of automobiles per capita?

25. Explain the term Thirty-nine Articles.

MISCELLANEOUS QUIZ NUMBER 8

The answer to Question Number one is what you have to have to get a good mark in all the other twenty-four. See page 227 for the right answers.

1. What does I.Q. stand for?
2. If two figures coincide when placed one upon the other, what are they called?
3. Which state has only three counties?
4. How is Eire pronounced?
5. From what language do we get most of our musical terms?
6. What is Olympus?
7. To what Jewish tribe did Paul belong?
8. In Dickens' "Tale of Two Cities," what are the cities?
9. What does "Honi soit qui mal y pense" mean?
10. Where is the Gibraltar of America?
11. How long will grape vines produce?
12. What is a nom de plume?
13. What are the two leading universities of England?
14. How many degrees are there in a circle?
15. Why is cognac so called?

16. Blue Birds refers to what girls' organization?
17. Who mourned because he had no more worlds to conquer?
18. For what is Rue de la Paix famous?
19. Where are the Lipari Islands?
20. From what are pearl buttons made?
21. Explain the difference between the prefixes ante and anti.
22. What are the Aldine Editions?
23. Whence come the words, "So shines a good deed in a naughty world"?
24. Which of the following are fresh water fish: perch, shad, pike, salmon?
25. How many links are there in a chain?

MISCELLANEOUS QUIZ NUMBER 9

The gentleman who used the expression in Question Number eleven must have been a Quizitor in his day, for you can't exist very long in a Quiz without thinking. (Answers on page 228.)

1. Where is the baseball Hall of Fame?
2. How long has the name British Commonwealth of Nations been used?
3. Define "a better 'ole."
4. What is the symbolism of the pomegranate in art?
5. How old was the new President of Ireland when he assumed office?
6. What are British consols?
7. Did a Roman Catholic Cardinal ever become King?
8. Why was it said that Draco's Code was written in blood?
9. In which House of the British Parliament do members wear their hats and why?
10. The ruler of what great European state is a vegetarian?
11. Who said, "I think, therefore I exist?"

13. What is the oldest newspaper feature now running?

14. Distinguish between stalagmite and stalactite.

15. What character in mythology had 100 eyes, and what happened to them?

16. Give the name of England's best-known humorous magazine.

17. By what name was King Arthur's sword known?

18. What term describes a victory that is disastrous to the victor as well as vanquished?

19. Is there a country in which there are no cemeteries?

20. What State observes Fast Day as an annual holiday?

21. What historic building in Massachusetts was built from money collected through lotteries?

22. Is a rare stamp more valuable if it is on its original envelope?

23. Name the seven deadly sins.

24. What newspaper has the largest circulation in the world?

25. What cities were from ancient times famous for the quality of their steel weapons?

MISCELLANEOUS QUIZ NUMBER 11

Quiz Number Eleven is your lucky number. Time bogey is five minutes. And the answers are on page 229.

1. Who wrote the poem, "I Shall Not Pass Again This Way?"
2. When is the abbreviation Ms. placed before a woman's name on a letter?
3. Upon what does Bermuda depend for its entire water supply?
4. Who is the Henry Ford of France?
5. What is the name of the American ship that mysteriously disappeared in 1918?
6. Who was the Roman noted for his elaborate banquets?
7. Who presented Jenny Lind to the American public?
8. Where are the highest tides on the Pacific Coast?
9. Nell Gwynn was the favorite of which English King?
10. To what does "Ides of March" refer?
11. Approximately how long is the Lincoln Highway?
12. Who was the noted illustrator of "Alice in Wonderland?"

13. What well-known war correspondent was the first rapid-fire newscaster?

14. What gifts did the Three Wise Men bring to the infant Jesus?

15. Who was the American poet who walked through the Middle West, "taking neither purse nor scrip with him?"

16. An Italian coming to the United States to live is called an immigrant or an emigrant?

17. Name the ship on which Napoleon took refuge after the Battle of Waterloo?

18. In what country did the Boxer Rebellion occur?

19. Name the fashionable residential section of London, north of Buckingham Palace and east of Hyde Park.

20. The capital of Missouri is St. Louis, Jefferson City, or Kansas City?

21. Who was the American General at the Battle of New Orleans—Andrew Johnson, Andrew Jackson or Benjamin Harrison?

22. The official colors of which of the following colleges are gold and blue: Cornell, Harvard, Princeton, Notre Dame?

23. Which weighs less, damp air or dry air?

24. The subject of what world famous picture has no eyebrows?

25. What is another name for Helvetia?

MISCELLANEOUS QUIZ NUMBER 12

The female of the species may be less color-blind than the male, but she passes just as many red lights! (See page 230 for the answers.)

1. What recent successful play on Broadway had no hero?
2. Where can the original One Horse Shay be seen?
3. By whom was the word "glamour" first popularized?
4. The prologue to what opera is a famous baritone solo?
5. Who is William McChesney Martin, Jr.?
6. What State is noted for its colonels?
7. Mrs. John R. Marsh is the married name of the author of a best seller. Name it.
8. Why is the Saar Basin so important?
9. In which sex does color-blindness predominate?
10. What causes a stitch in the side?
11. Which is the second oldest college in the United States?
12. By whom were the Little Colonel books written?
13. Who was Nefertiti?

14. What instrument records earthquakes?

15. Name three poets who wrote while in prison.

16. Which port noted for its gold shipments, and mentioned in the Old Testament, is not on the map?

17. How long is the side of a square acre?

18. Define the word Messiah.

19. Who presided at the "Bloody Assizes?"

20. Name the versatile Englishman who sings, acts, and composes the music for his own plays.

21. A Princeton alumnus travels widely in far lands and writes books about his adventures. Who is he?

22. Which symphony is based on American folk tunes?

23. To what part of the world are coral reefs confined?

24. What holds the planets in place?

25. A Portuguese man-o-war is a fish or a ship?

MISCELLANEOUS QUIZ NUMBER 13

Watch out for Question Number 23. No, it isn't mountain music! The right answer is on page 230.

1. In what city is the Wailing Wall?
2. Which planet is surrounded by rings?
3. What is another name for the river Donau?
4. Where is the "Land of Cakes?"
5. Who painted the famous picture, "The Gleaners?"
6. Where is the largest stone in the world?
7. Which Five Towns are included in the Potteries in England?
8. Who was the Poet of the Sierras?
9. Locate, "Old Faithful."
10. Who were the Roundheads?
11. Which is the lightest of all known woods?
12. Name another noted portrait of an artist's mother, besides that of Whistler.
13. Who wrote under the pen name A. E.?
14. Where is the original Home Sweet Home?
15. What Nationality was John Calvin?
16. According to the old saying, see what city and die?
17. Where is the island of Majorca?

18. Whose residence was "Longwood," and where is it?
19. What is lava?
20. Key to the Mediterranean refers to what great fortress?
21. State the difference between meteors and meteorites.
22. Which is the only remaining wonder of the ancient world?
23. By what name is the study of mountains called?
24. By what unit is the speed of ships measured?
25. Which is the second largest State in the Union?

MISCELLANEOUS QUIZ NUMBER 14

We're all straight on Mark Twain and Mark Hanna and Mark Antony, but what we're worried about is what mark we're going to get on Quiz 14. We'll soon know when we look at page 231.

1. With whom do you associate the big stick? Little brown brother?
2. Name five popular heroes of the Spanish-American War.
3. Who was Mark Hanna?
4. Who were the Rough Riders?
5. Who is called the George Washington of South America?
6. How many cubic inches in a gallon?
7. Which is the Green Mountain State?
8. Who was Geronimo?
9. How many kinds of bees are there in every hive?
10. Which person led Bacon's Rebellion: Francis Bacon, Nathaniel Bacon, Roger Bacon?
11. What was a Sooner?
12. Who was President of the United States at the beginning of this century?
13. What was Mark Twain's real name?

14. Which President was born on Friday, inaugurated on Friday, died on Friday?
15. Which is the Sucker State?
16. What is the difference between a parabola and a parable?
17. Who wrote "The Female of the Species?"
18. Which of these are birds: flail, grail, quail, rail?
19. Which of these may be tobacco: grist, twist, wrist?
20. What is the difference between yellow jack and yellow jacket?
21. Who was William Crawford Gorgas?
22. What is the difference between rhinoceros and rhinitis?
23. What invention is associated with (1) Fitch; (2) Whitney; (3) Howe; (4) McCormick?
24. What was the Parthenon?
25. Who organized the Boston Tea Party?

MISCELLANEOUS QUIZ NUMBER 15

Did you ever pop the question to a Gibson Girl? Perhaps this Quiz will give her the chance to get back at you. (Correct answers on page 232.)

1. What three men concluded the treaty in which Great Britain recognized the independence of the United States?
2. What is meant by "playing 'possum?"
3. What state is known as The Old Dominion?
4. How large is the District of Columbia?
5. What American animal can hang by its tail?
6. What State is the Nutmeg State?
7. Where is Mesa Verde National Park?
8. What two men have each been nominated three times for the Presidency by the Democratic Party?
9. Which Presidents have been assassinated?
10. What claims to fame has Salem, Illinois?
11. Who wrote (1) "Progress and Poverty"; (2) "Looking Backward?"
12. What was Coxey's Army?
13. Who was Charles Dana Gibson?
14. Who was Sequoyah?

15. With whom do you associate (1) "The Man With the Hoe;" (2) "The Melting Pot?"

16. In which campaign was the Full Dinner Pail a slogan?

17. How do ants communicate with each other?

18. What is the present name of the Patrons of Husbandry?

19. How many pounds of milk does a cow produce in a year?

20. Which is the Hawkeye State?

21. What is HCl; H_2O; NaCl?

22. What is Aconcagua?

23. What was the Acropolis?

24. To which country does each of the following coins belong: (a) guilder, (b) franc, (c) gourde?

25. What woman was authorized by Congress to wear men's clothes?

MISCELLANEOUS QUIZ NUMBER 16

You, too, may be the big gun in your neighborhood by making up a percentage of 100 for this Quiz. There's only one tough question—number 22. At least it seemed tough 38 years ago! (Answers on page 232.)

1. Give the correct pronunciation of rodeo.
2. What is the name of the famous convict ship that occasionally visits this country?
3. Who walked across the United States when he was 70 years old?
4. What method of execution has recently been put into use in several States?
5. Who painted the "Boy with the Rabbit?"
6. Name the two most important fur-bearing animals.
7. What is the oldest form of gambling?
8. Who was known as the Lion of the North?
9. What is a chinquapin?
10. Braille is what kind of type?
11. What author was born in Scotland and died in Samoa?
12. What are junks?
13. Name the ornamental tree that blossoms but bears no fruit.

14. Who was known as the last of the great scouts?
15. What makes day and night?
16. With what implement does a Chinaman eat his food?
17. Define the word tycoon.
18. What was Paul Revere's occupation?
19. Give another name for the Renaissance.
20. What were daguerrotypes?
21. With what sport is Glenna Collett associated?
22. Did the Twentieth Century begin January 1, 1900, or January 1, 1901?
23. In what city is the Kremlin?
24. How many pounds in a long ton?
25. What German woman gave her name to a long-range gun?

MISCELLANEOUS QUIZ NUMBER 17

This one looks easy, but there are several stingers sand-wiched in between the softies. The correct answers may be found on page 233.

1. Where is Curaçao, and to what nation does it belong?
2. What happened to the old cruiser *Cuba* sunk in the Spanish-American War of 1898?
3. Who was General Juan Vicente Gomez?
4. Who wrote and issued the famous "Poor Richard's Almanac?"
5. Where is the world's greatest horse and mule market located?
6. Who was Emile Zola?
7. Which is considered to be James A. M. Whistler's most celebrated painting?
8. What are known as the seven ancient wonders of the world?
9. Which verse in the Bible contains the complete alphabet?
10. To whom does the Territory of the Yukon belong?
11. What and where is the Hall of Fame?
12. What is meant by Hobson's choice?

13. What President of the United States was nicknamed "Old Rough and Ready"?

14. What is Noah Webster noted for?

15. Around what fairy tale did Engelbert Humperdinck write a famous opera?

16. For what instrument chiefly did Frederic François Chopin write?

17. What is adobe?

18. What is a campanile?

19. What is a cameo?

20. Where is the highest point in the United States?

21. What coal tar product is 500 times sweeter than sugar?

22. In what human gland is iodine normally found?

23. What are homonyms?

24. What was Ulysses S. Grant's given name?

25. What is the famous inscription on the Liberty Bell in Independence Hall, Philadelphia and where was it taken from?

MISCELLANEOUS QUIZ NUMBER 18

"M.Q." after your name stands for Master Quizisist, and means that you have scored 100 in Miscellaneous Quiz Number 18. Check your answers with those on page 234.

1. What is the smallest republic in the world?
2. Name the most famous married couple on the American stage.
3. Give the authors of the popular books, "How to Win Friends and Influence People," and "How to Lose Friends and Alienate People"?
4. Who is the most celebrated young Jewish violinist?
5. What Governor is nicknamed "Happy"?
6. Who is associated with the inception of the Tennessee Valley Authority?
7. Was it Andrew Mellon or John D. Rockefeller, Jr., who decided to restore Williamsburg, Virginia?
8. Does the word labial pertain to the eyes, ears, nose or lips?
9. Where are Panama hats made?
10. What poet awoke one morning to find himself famous?
11. What is a crinoline?

12. Which is the most popular beverage in the world?

13. What kind of leather is most extensively used for gloves?

14. What office does Robert H. Jackson hold?

15. What was the first metal used by man?

16. Which runs the long way of a fabric—the warp or the woof?

17. Give the name for the musical composition that expresses ecstasy or joy.

18. What commercial resin is obtained from insects?

19. What are the Romance languages?

20. Where is the largest baseball park?

21. Explain M.P. used after an Englishman's name.

22. Finish the saying, *"Where ignorance is bliss ...."*

23. Why are day dreams called castles in Spain?

24. What is Yom Kippur?

25. State the distinguishing feature of Gothic architecture.

MISCELLANEOUS QUIZ NUMBER 19

One of the duties of the Ogpu is to check on Quizzers who look at the back of the book before they honestly try to answer all the questions themselves. (By back of the book we mean page 234.)

1. How does the cricket make his chirping sounds?
2. For what is the Pulitzer Prize in literature given?
3. Where is the most gold found?
4. What is the Holy Grail?
5. Are the United States lighthouses all the same color?
6. In what city is Limehouse?
7. Why was the Crystal Palace in London so called?
8. What is the name of Soviet Russia's secret service organization?
9. Why is the fourth Sunday in Lent called Refreshment Sunday?
10. What animal washes its food?
11. Why is the Adam's apple so called?
12. If a baby is to have "Jr." after his name, must he have the same middle name that his father bears?
13. How long after marriage is the wife considered a bride?

14. Where is the Maelstrom?
15. Who wrote the poem, "Mother O'Mine"?
16. Is the "funny bone" really a bone?
17. What is a dory?   A droshky?
18. What advertising sign illuminates the Eiffel Tower?
19. What was the first modern detective story?
20. When was the liberty motor perfected?
21. Who is the patron saint of farmers?
22. How many seasons must a flower grow to be a perennial?
23. What is the well-known fish, sometimes called the lamprey, which is the crossword puzzlers delight?
24. What are Annie Oakleys?
25. Which is the cheaper source of illumination, candle or kerosene lamp?

MISCELLANEOUS QUIZ NUMBER 20

If your answers are all "comme il faut," you will be able to chalk up a perfect score for Quiz Number 20. (You will find the correct answers on page 235.)

1. What is the name given to a woman hater?
2. Which poet was known as Ariel?
3. What is the difference between a redan and a sedan?
4. How fast was Walter Johnson's pitched ball?
5. What is the holy-ghost flower?
6. To whom did Walt Whitman refer when he wrote "O Captain, My Captain"?
7. Which President of the United States taught in a school for the blind?
8. With what famous character is a lantern associated?
9. What leader conducts an all-feminine orchestra?
10. Which European country has the most lakes?
11. Who was the flyer lost ten years ago in South American jungles for whom many have searched?
12. Who was Parson Weems, and for what is he remembered?
13. Who was the ploughboy poet?
14. Who were the twin sons of Zeus by a human mother?

15. How much does a gallon of water weigh?
16. Who was Joseph Pulitzer?
17. What State had the Bear Flag?
18. If a bamboo is not a tree, what is it?
19. What is the northernmost great city of the world?
20. Name the famous columnist who broadcasts for Jergen's lotion.
21. In the skull and crossbones what bones are represented?
22. Approximately how far does the postman walk on an average day?
23. What does, "comme il faut" mean?
24. What is a "dipsy do"?
25. Who is the Sage of Potato Hill?

MISCELLANEOUS QUIZ NUMBER 21

Miscellaneous comes from a Latin word meaning mixed. This Quiz is surely a mixture—all the way from Cape Flattery to Proxima Centauri. (Answers on page 236.)

1. Who was the prince who led his army from a sick bed?
2. Who was the Ambassador of Good Will?
3. Which nation has two-fifths of the world's movie theatres?
4. Name the two points in the United States that are farthest apart.
5. What does Mikado mean?
6. Whose name has become a symbol for discipline?
7. What radio personality was born in Baku, Russia?
8. What is the Mason and Dixon Line?
9. In what connection was the slogan, "Out of the trenches by Christmas," used?
10. By what name was M. Buonarroti generally known?
11. For whom was Harper's Ferry, West Virginia, named?
12. In what poem occurs the character "the lady that's known as Lou"?

13. What is a male bee called?
14. In what language did Horace write?
15. Who received the title "Lady with the Lamp"?
16. Which English King knighted a loin of beef?
17. What newspaper was known as The Thunderer?
18. In what building are the British Crown Jewels kept?
19. Next to the sun, which is our nearest star?
20. For what is Sèvres noted?
21. Give the origin of the word plagiarism.
22. What nationality is the flyer who set the present world's speed record for airplanes?
23. For what does G.A.R. stand?
24. Which is the Pelican State?
25. Give some of the early names to describe a motion picture apparatus.

MISCELLANEOUS QUIZ NUMBER 22

What is the Agony Column? Well, from all of the groaning and moaning we hear, it might be any page of this book! You can end the agony by looking on page 236.

1. What tree may have several thousand trunks?
2. What is the Agony Column?
3. Is Vladivostok far north in relation to European cities?
4. What is wind?
5. What is broadloom carpet?
6. Why are turkish towels so named?
7. What is the fandango?
8. Is the Red Sea red?
9. What words in the English language rhyme with month?
10. Whose voice was as loud as that of 50 men?
11. Are pointed furs natural?
12. What is the parting salutation that we get from the Old Testament?
13. Which is the largest inland body of water below sea level?
14. To what does sporran refer?

15. For whom was the Hudson River named?
16. Where do most earthquakes occur in America?
17. Where was Joan of Arc born?
18. What word denotes exaggerated devotion to one's country?
19. Where is the Lake of Pitch; who discovered it?
20. A says Winston Churchill is an American author. B says Winston Churchill is a British politician. Which is right?
21. Reclaimed or rewoven wool is known by what name?
22. Is standard time now kept all over the world?
23. Which is the Lone Star State?
24. Where is Sam Houston National Forest?
25. Give five words that are either surnames or coined from surnames.   Example: Listerine, pasteurize.

MISCELLANEOUS QUIZ NUMBER 23

And so we come to the last of our Quizzes. We hope you have enjoyed the fun, and that the wear and tear on your thinkery hasn't been too strenuous. We hope, too, that in matching your wits with the Question-and-Answer Man you have learned a great many things you never knew before. (Answers on page 237.)

1. Estimate the present population of the world.
2. From what play are the lines, "Hath not a Jew eyes, Hath not a Jew hands"?
3. Why are members of Congress spoken of as solons?
4. And all the days of Methuselah were .... how many years?
5. What is meant by pump priming?
6. Can anything be wider than it is long?
7. Name the highest point in Africa.
8. May crisp bacon be eaten with the fingers?
9. What day is the first Tuesday after the first Monday in November?
10. Which animal has the ability to feign death when in danger?
11. Name the three types of musical instruments.

12. Finish the line: "Train up a child in the way he should go and ...."

13. What was the first all-talking picture?

14. What announcer has been on the air longest?

15. Where is the father of the young Archduke Otto of Hapsburg buried?

16. By whom were the following words uttered, "Had I but served my God with half the zeal I served my King ...."?

17. By whom was the Law of Gravitation discovered?

18. Who composed the famous Largo from "Xerxes"?

19. What is the source of the quotation, "When I use a word it means what I choose it to mean"?

20. Name the President of the Radio Corporation of America.

21. For what does F.F.V. stand?

22. The autograph of which Signer of the Declaration of Independence commands the highest price?

23. Who was the poet who composed a noted poem in a dream and wrote it the next morning?

24. What is the average daily expenditure of an automobile tourist?

25. Identify the following contemporary women: (1) Mary E. Woolley; (2) Edith Nourse Rogers; (3) Elizabeth Hawes; (4) Marya Zaturenska; (5) Florence Jaffray Harriman; (6) Mary Margaret McBride.

ANSWERS

ART QUIZ NUMBER 1

1. Andrea del Sarto.
2. Sistine Madonna.
3. Cubism.
4. Whistler.
5. Sir Joshua Reynolds.
6. "Portal of Hell," a bronze door for the Museum of Decorative Art in Paris.
7. "Mona Lisa."
8. "The Anatomy Lesson," by Rembrandt.
9. To indicate that they were alive when the painting was executed.
10. Saint-Gaudens.
11. The Norman Conquest of England and the events leading up to it.
12. Yes, on the wall of the refectory of the Convent of Santa Maria delle Grazie in Milan.
13. Greek sculptor. About 340 B.C.
14. Titian.
15. He painted it. Often abbreviated pinx.
16. Millet.

17. Sculpture, engraving and gold-smithing.
18. Rosa Bonheur.
19. Albrecht Dürer.
20. Stuart because he was vain and Botticelli because he was modest.
21. Painting of inanimate objects or groups of objects.
22. Tapestry. The Gobelin tapestries excel everything of the kind in Europe.
23. A circular window filled with tracery.
24. Golden Gate Park, San Francisco. It is by James E. Fraser.
25. The artist's real name was Jacopo Robusti. He was called Tintoretto—little dyer —from his father's trade.

ART QUIZ NUMBER 2

1. Water spouts, often grotesquely carved, placed on the roof gutters of Gothic buildings.
2. The principal front of a building.

3. "The Pot of Basil" by John W. Alexander.

4. A stone carved in the form of a beetle.

5. The painter wished to keep it in his studio as a nest egg from which to make copies.

6. John Francis Murphy, American landscape painter.

7. This story is told of Zeuxis, Greek painter of the 5th century B.C.

8. Sir Christopher Wren. The words are an inscription in St. Paul's Cathedral, London.

9. Not as we know it today. It was deep crimson.

10. Low relief, sculpture in which the figures project less than half their apparent total thickness.

11. George Catlin. (1796–1872).

12. Millet; Rubens; Botticelli; Bonheur.

13. The making of stained glass windows.

14. Tyrian purple, Damascus steel and malleable glass.

15. It is the only marble statue with eyelashes.

16. Atlantes or Telamones.

17. The making of pottery.

18. No. It received its name from Sir Joshua Reynolds because upon its discovery the picture was so dimmed and defaced by time that it looked like a night scene. After cleaning, it was found to represent a scene in broad day.

19. Joaquin Sorolla y Bastida (1863–1923).

20. Jose Maria Sert.

21. Famous variety of Japanese pottery.

22. On a cloudy day.

23. It is an Italian word meaning the child or babe, and refers to representations in art of the infant Christ in swaddling clothes.

24. The amount of light and dark, the greater the amount of light the higher the value; the greater the amount of dark the lower the value.

25. Spain. It is the Alhambra in Granada.

WORLD HISTORY QUIZ
NUMBER 1

1. Fifty-six.

2. Herbert Hoover. In Iowa.

3. The lower house of the legislature of the Irish Free State.

4. Peter Stuyvesant.

5. Battle of New Orleans, January 8, 1815, was fought after the Treaty of Ghent, December 24, 1814.

6. An ultimatum offered in

1775 to England by the American Colonies. It was rejected.

7. The period between March 20, 1815, when Napoleon arrived in Paris from Elba, and June 28, 1815, the restoration of Louis XVIII.

8. Ethan Allen and the Green Mountain Boys, May 10, 1775.

9. Oliver Cromwell.

10. Bismarck.

11. Von Steuben, Lafayette, Rochambeau, Pulaski, Kosciusko, DeKalb.

12. Calvin Coolidge.

13. King of Sweden, Italian statesman, Greek writer, Roman Emperor.

14. Woodrow Wilson in addressing Congress, January 8, 1918, named fourteen points as essential to a consideration of peace.

15. Massacre of Huguenots on August 24, 1572 in Paris under Charles IX.

16. George I.

17. Austerlitz, 1805. The emperors were Napoleon I, Alexander I of Russia and Francis II of Austria.

18. Catherine of Aragon, Anne Boleyn, Jane Seymour, Anne of Cleves, Catherine Howard, Catherine Parr.

19. November 24, 1863. Lookout Mountain.

20. Virginia. Elizabeth was known as the Virgin Queen.

21. No. It was preceded by New York and Philadelphia.

22. Waterloo, 1814.

23. A state erected by Japan in 1932, out of Chinese territory, formerly Manchuria.

24. The golden in 1887, and the diamond in 1897.

25. Henry IV of France. In 1589.

WORLD HISTORY QUIZ NUMBER 2

1. Egbert. He reigned from 827–839.

2. The American Revolution.

3. The followers of Stephen A. Douglas who was nicknamed Little Giant because of his small stature and great mental powers.

4. The Jameson Raid on Johannesburg (1895–96) led by a British subject, Dr. L. S. Jameson. The raiders were defeated and Jameson captured.

5. Men who, during the Civil War, hid themselves in swamps to avoid being drafted into the Southern Army.

6. 1746. The Battle of Culloden.

7. A small chamber in the old fort at Calcutta in which a whole British garrison was confined on June 20, 1756 by the Nawab of Bengal. 123 died before morning of suffocation.

8. The Persians.

9. Lady Jane Grey.

10. Monroe's. It was the period between 1817 and 1823.

11. The English barons forced King John to sign the Magna Charta on June 15, 1215.

12. At the Peace Conference of 1919, France, Great Britain, Italy, Japan, United States, or their representatives, Clemenceau, Lloyd-George, Orlando, Makino and Wilson.

13. Coup d'état.

14. General Allenby.

15. Herodotus. (484–425 B.C.)

16. Geneva, Switzerland.

17. The Copperheads.

18. Germany.

19. Cambridge, Massachusetts.

20. No, only since 1905, when she declared her independence of Sweden.

21. The Senators who engaged in filibuster to defeat the Armed Neutrality Bill.

22. He crossed the Alps into Italy with full baggage train and elephants during the Second Punic War (218–201 B.C.)

23. An assembly in the city of Worms, Germany, convened in 1521 to check the Reformation.

24. Article I, Section 8, Paragraph 18. The words "necessary and proper" permit great differences in interpretation by the strict constructionists and the loose constructionists.

25. Great Britain, France. It was signed April 8, 1904. In 1907 the Entente Cordiale developed into the Triple Entente, when Russia joined the alliance.

BIOGRAPHY QUIZ NUMBER 1

1. Marco Polo. The statue is at Soochow.

2. General Francis Marion.

3. Thomas Edward Lawrence, Lawrence of Arabia.

4. He was drowned when the Cruiser Hampshire sunk in 1916 while en route to Russia.

5. Medina, Arabia.

6. Journalism.

7. Sir Richard Francis Burton (1821–1890).

8. According to Plutarch, from

the bite of an asp, conveyed to her in a basket of fruit.

9. Artemus Ward.

10. Yes, a withered arm.

11. Benjamin Disraeli. He became premier in 1868.

12. Einstein is a famous physicist, Epstein a sculptor.

13. George Bernard Shaw, Irish playwright.

14. Julius Caesar.

15. Russian monk, who exercised a strong influence over the last Czarina of Russia.

16. Peter Abelard. His pupil was Heloise.

17. Mrs. Nicholas Longworth, daughter of Theodore Roosevelt.

18. Andrew Carnegie.

19. Lola Montez. Mistress of Louis I of Bavaria.

20. Elizabeth, Queen of Roumania (1843–1916).

21. Francis II of France, Lord Darnley, the Earl of Bothwell.

22. Parisian dress designer.

23. Mary, Queen of Scots. They were her ladies-in-waiting.

24. North Elba, New York.

25. Nathan Hale.

BIOGRAPHY QUIZ NUMBER 2

1. Joseph Patrick Kennedy.

2. Friedrich Ebert. (1919–1925)

3. Gustavus III of Sweden, in 1792.

4. Salome.

5. First Atlantic telegraph cable.

6. Admiral Nicholas Horthy of Hungary.

7. Cecil John Rhodes.

8. Kindergarten method of teaching.

9. William, Prince of Orange, (1650–1702), Stadtholder of the Netherlands.

10. Sir Francis Drake. The expression means that, as an English Admiral, he so frequently defeated the Spanish navy, carrying his daring attacks into the very Spanish ports where the Armada was being built.

11. Macedonia. Born in 356 B.C. Died 323 B.C.

12. Ballet dancing.

13. Jean Paul Marat was stabbed by Charlotte Corday in 1793.

14. He was the only English Pope. As Adrian IV he ruled from 1154 to 1159.

15. Yes, she was queen of the British tribe Iceni during the first century A.D.

16. Twelve years.

17. Democritus, Greek philosopher, was so-called. (460–362 B.C.)

18. Frederick I, Barbarossa. He ruled from 1152–1190.
19. No, in New York City, in 1882.
20. In the sinking of the *Lusitania,* May 7, 1915.
21. "More light."
22. The Brontës, Charlotte, Emily and Anne.
23. Georges Clemenceau, French statesman.
24. Lord Nelson, hero of the Battle of the Nile and Trafalgar.
25. Caroline Amelia Elizabeth, wife of George IV. She died in 1821.

BIBLE QUIZ NUMBER 1

1. Twice, in Matthew VI and St. Luke XI.
2. Literally it means rule or measure. In reference to the Bible it means those books which were accepted as inspired.
3. Malchus, servant of the high priest.
4. Joshua.
5. Solomon.
6. Gopher wood.
7. Forty-three.
8. It was given by Pharaoh to Jacob and his family.
9. Job.
10. The Old Testament in Greek. Tradition says there were seventy translators.
11. The Four Horsemen of the Apocalypse by Vincente Blasco Ibañez.
12. The 117th.
13. Elijah.
14. God with us.
15. I Corinthians 13.
16. Tentmaker.
17. Yes. The King James Bible came to be known as the Authorized Version because on the title page was the line, "Appointed to be read in churches."
18. It was destroyed, hidden or stolen during the capture of Jerusalem by Nebuchadnezzar and has never been seen since.
19. Nicodemus.
20. On Mt. Ararat.
21. A mess of pottage.
22. Psalms such as the 119th in which the verses of successive portions are arranged in alphabetical order.
23. Nine years; from 1523 to 1532.
24. Elisha brought back to life the child of the Shunammite.
25. St. Luke says that He was about thirty years old.

BIBLE QUIZ NUMBER 2

1. He once wrote on the ground with His finger but it is not

known what that writing was.

2. The witch of Endor.
3. John the Baptist.
4. The distance that might be traveled on the Sabbath usually 2,000 cubits.
5. In the Sermon on the Mount.
6. Jael drove a nail into his forehead while he slept.
7. She was turned into a pillar of salt.
8. Peter.
9. Belshazzar.
10. Mary of Bethany.
11. In a whirlwind.
12. Honor thy father and thy mother, that thy days may be long upon the land which the Lord thy God giveth thee.
13. James and John; Simon Peter and Andrew.
14. No.
15. Matthew 7:12. All things whatsoever ye would that men should do unto you, do ye even so to them.
16. The first five books of the Old Testament: Genesis, Exodus, Leviticus, Numbers, Deuteronomy.
17. Isaiah, Jeremiah, Ezekiel, Daniel.
18. John the Baptist.
19. St. Mark.
20. He was let down from a window in a basket.

21. David.
22. Forty.
23. Mary Magdalene.
24. The Standard Latin Version of the Bible. The term is derived from the Latin word meaning multitude. St. Jerome made the translation in the 4th century.
25. A title of God in Revelations, meaning the beginning and the end.

SPORTS AND GAMES QUIZ NUMBER 1

1. 1875.
2. Ice hockey.
3. Sixty in 1927.
4. Cricket.
5. Originally it was run between two prominent objects such as steeples.
6. Hershey, Pennsylvania.
7. Chukkers.
8. Bull fighting.
9. In 1921, 1922, 1923, 1936 and 1937.
10. Lacrosse.
11. About 13½ pounds.
12. The name is believed to be derived from the Persian Shah, meaning king.
13. Voss, Norway.
14. Man O'War.
15. Cleveland, Washington, St. Louis, Detroit.
16. Heavyweight.

17. The Thames.
18. Cork. It is about the size of a marble, and the cork is aged for 15 years.
19. The crawl.
20. Tom Heeney in 1928.
21. Seymour Dunn.
22. Disraeli.
23. Berlin, Germany.
24. Charlie Gehringer of the Detroit Americans.
25. 1926.

Sports and Games Quiz Number 2

1. About 6 feet 1½ inches.
2. Bowling out three players with successive pitches.
3. Four—at each base.
4. The player having the first move.
5. Creel.
6. No, it could not, since this is a race for 3-year olds.
7. In Chicago.
8. Skiing.
9. Three minutes.
10. It is a circus term for a sold-out performance.
11. Yacht racing.
12. Five of a kind is the highest hand.
13. Hickory.
14. Judge Kenesaw Mountain Landis.
15. It closes the doubling but not the bidding.

16. A pass of an opponent's bid made with the purpose of letting the opponents reach a contract which can be penalized profitably.
17. Zev, Grey Lag, Mad Play, Sir Barton, Cudgel, Mad Hatter, Chance Shot, Flying Ebony.
18. It is said to be the hand held by Wild Bill Hickok when he was shot in 1876.
19. Lawn tennis.
20. Six.
21. It counts 29.
22. James J. Corbett.
23. In reference to Joseph Grimaldi, the famous English clown (1779–1837).
24. The service.
25. About 20 feet ahead.

Politics and Government Quiz Number 1

1. The mace.
2. Left wing politicians or members of a legislature are liberal or radical, right wing members are conservative.
3. Twelve. Georgia was not represented.
4. Greece. Hellas is the Greek name of the country.
5. Yes, from 1871 to 1875.
6. Nicholas Murray Butler.
7. John Quincy Adams not only suggested but also formulated it.

8. Seven years.
9. In the election of 1880 supporting the candidacy of General Hancock.
10. Since the exposure of the Tweed ring in New York City in 1872.
11. Six. Three were assassinated.
12. No.
13. 280,674.
14. Senator Borah of Idaho, who has served continuously since March 4, 1907.
15. Persia.
16. The late Percy L. Gassaway of Oklahoma.
17. Connecticut, Rhode Island, New Mexico.
18. No, but it is customary. The Constitution provides only that the House shall choose its Speaker.
19. The National Socialist German Labor Party (Nazi) was founded in 1920 in Munich by Hitler.
20. No, a rule of the Senate forbids it.
21. A clause introduced by David Wilmot as an amendment to a bill in 1846. It provided for prohibition of slavery in all territory to be acquired from Mexico.
22. Britain.
23. The right side considered from the Speaker's desk, facing the House.
24. Poland.
25. It is sent to the Department of State.

POLITICS AND GOVERNMENT
QUIZ NUMBER 2

1. Yes, on November 16, 1933.
2. Yes. President Wilson on April 2, 1917 asked for a declaration of war against Germany.
3. Eleven. (As of 1938)
4. A de facto government is one actually exercising governing power; a de jure government is one which exists by legal right or international recognition.
5. No. There is no law which requires the attendance of a Member of Congress at any session.
6. John Brown (1757–1837).
7. The Democratic Party.
8. He is not. The Framers purposely omitted such a reference.
9. No, they are appointed by the President and confirmed by the Senate.
10. Three: the Adams, Harrison and Roosevelt families.
11. Government by a few.
12. Chancellor of the Exchequer.

13. The State of Vatican City whose area is 108.7 acres.
14. Judge Nathan Miller of New York.
15. No. Justice George Sutherland was born in England.
16. King of the Belgians.
17. William Jennings Bryan was only 36 when nominated in 1896.
18. Quebec.
19. Money used to influence votes or legislation.
20. Wisconsin, Minnesota, North Dakota. (As of 1938.)
21. John Jay.
22. According to a published opinion of the State Department in 1932, there were not.
23. J. Ramsay MacDonald.
24. Justice Hugo L. Black who is 52 years old. (As of 1938)
25. Zachary Taylor.

9. Hippopotamus.
10. The ostrich.
11. About 92.4 per cent.
12. The horned toad will do this when alarmed.
13. Because its leaves turn their edges north and south and so indicate direction.
14. The beaver.
15. Forget-me-not.
16. No, a live lobster is greenish brown.
17. The humming bird is the only one, it can fly backward as well as forward.
18. Fruit, stem, flower, head.
19. Flock, covey, school, swarm.
20. White. The stripes are black or dark brown.
21. Amphibians.
22. Underground.
23. Probably because of their inability to carry sap to greater heights.
24. The bat.
25. Guano.

Natural History Quiz Number 1

1. The sloth.
2. The thistle family.
3. The hyrax.
4. Animal.
5. Linnaeus.
6. A fish.
7. The raccoon.
8. No.

Natural History Quiz Number 2

1. The giant tortoise. It may live as long as 200 years.
2. The mule.
3. Ants.
4. Boar, hippopotamus, walrus.
5. The Rose family.
6. Holland.
7. The rat.

8. A load 15 or 20 times its own weight.
9. Guinea-pigs.
10. Although it is a conifer it sheds its needles every year.
11. Female.
12. The Judas tree.
13. Because it flashes a red light at the ends of the body and a green light along the sides.
14. The secretary bird.
15. Yes, mahogany trees are cut by moonlight for then the tree is freer from sap, sounder and of richer color.
16. The hare.
17. The opossum.
18. To keep cool.
19. The ostrich.
20. They have no green coloring matter or chlorophyll.
21. The cormorant.
22. The amoeba.
23. Animals that have an abdominal pouch for carrying their young, such as the kangaroo.
24. The sapwood is practically white, only the heartwood is black.
25. Animals.

LITERATURE AND LANGUAGE
QUIZ NUMBER 1

1. The Bible.
2. Jules Verne in his book "Twenty Thousand Leagues Under the Sea," written in 1869–70.
3. "Ben Hur," by Lew Wallace.
4. The letter E.
5. It is often attributed to Mark Twain, but originated with his friend Charles Dudley Warner. The expression appeared on the editorial page of the Hartford Courant.
6. Cyrano de Bergerac, hero of the drama by Edmond Rostand.
7. As computed by officers of the French Academy the number is 2796.
8. "David Copperfield."
9. Westminster Abbey, London.
10. Ralph Waldo Emerson.
11. Esperanto.
12. The Tam O' Shanter.
13. Palindrome.
14. John Keats. It is "Here lies one whose name was writ in water."
15. Archibald James Cronin, author of "the Citadel."
16. No. They occur in a sermon preached by Charles Wesley.
17. John Buchan, Lord Tweedsmuir, Governor-General of Canada.
18. "Lines on the Antiquity of Microbes," by Strickland

Gillilan, "Adam-Had'em."

19. Francois Marie Arouet.

20. There are only 44.

21. "The World in a Man of War," written in 1850.

22. Darby and Joan; Aucassin and Nicolette; Lancelot and Guinevere; Tristram and Iseult; Ben Hur and Esther; Gabriel and Evangeline; Orpheus and Eurydice; Paul and Virginia; Pyramus and Thisbe; Hiawatha and Minnehaha.

23. Alpha and Beta, the first and second letters of the Greek alphabet.

24. Representative John S. McGroarty of California entitled, "The Lady Eleanor."

25. Finley Peter Dunne.

LITERATURE AND LANGUAGE QUIZ NUMBER 2

1. Alexandre Dumas and Alexandre Dumas, fils.

2. Lafcadio Hearn (1850–1904.)

3. James Bryce, Viscount Bryce.

4. It means to expurgate. From Thomas Bowdler who in 1818 put out an expurgated edition of Shakespeare.

5. William de Morgan (1839–1917).

6. From a fairy tale by Hans Christian Anderson.

7. Euclid.

8. No. Philip Nolan was a fictitious character. The book is by Edward Everett Hale and was published in 1863.

9. From the "Uncle Remus" stories by Joel Chandler Harris.

10. It is not known when or by whom the phrase was coined. It was current in the Colonies before the Revolution.

11. Rabindranath Tagore.

12. Samuel Langhorne Clemens.

13. Athos, Porthos and Aramis. They appear in "The Three Musketeers" and other novels by Dumas.

14. Joseph Conrad (1857–1924). He was Polish by birth.

15. O. Henry, whose real name was William Sydney Porter.

16. Yes, Jonathan Swift's "Gulliver's Travels."

17. Joseph. His full name was Joseph Rudyard Kipling.

18. The phrase is attributed to Samuel Adams as early as 1776.

19. Hamlet. His lines number 1569.

20. The—not ye. The y is a

corruption of the old thorn letter, a symbol for th.

21. Oscar Wilde's Ballad of Reading Gaol.
22. Stockton's, "The Lady or the Tiger."
23. No, he was drowned and his remains cremated upon the shore of Italy.
24. Three: German, French and Italian.
25. The words that contain the vowels in their order are abstemious and facetious. Some other words, but not in natural order, are: authoritative, disadvantageous, efficacious, encouraging, importunate, and instantaneous.

Music Quiz Number 1

1. Francis Hopkinson.
2. Violoncello.
3. Haydn.
4. A sacred song for chorus, introduced by Martin Luther into the reformed church service.
5. The Battle of Borodino and Napoleon's unsuccessful invasion of Russia.
6. Chopin.
7. "Girl of the Golden West."
8. Nürnberg, Germany.
9. Approximately eight weeks.
10. Choir; e.g., string choir, woodwind choir, brass choir.

11. A popular concert. The expression originated in Boston.
12. Bidu Sayao.
13. Johann Sebastian Bach.
14. He became deaf when about 30 and composed most of his great symphonies thereafter.
15. An arrangement of four voices so that the tenor and soprano are not more than an octave apart.
16. Marcia Davenport, daughter of Alma Gluck, published "Of Lena Geyer" in 1936.
17. John Philip Sousa.
18. Castanets.
19. The harmonium.
20. "Das Rheingold," "Die Walküre," "Siegfried," "Götterdämmerung."
21. "Veni Creator Spiritus."
22. George Frederic Handel.
23. It was originally used for the Hundredth Psalm.
24. The text or words.
25. Franz Peter Schubert.

Music Quiz Number 2

1. Eight.
2. Rimsky-Korsakov.
3. "Rigoletto."
4. "Stars and Stripes Forever," by John Philip Sousa.
5. Japan.
6. Jan Sibelius.
7. "Turandot." It was fin-

ished by Alfano, and pro-
duced at LaScala, April 25,
1926.

8. Wagner.

9. Edward MacDowell. Mar-
ian Nevins MacDowell es-
tablished a music colony at
their summer home in Peter-
boro, New Hampshire.

10. The pipe organ.

11. This Hungarian dance takes
its name from an inn outside
the city of Budapest.

12. Yes. "Le Roi S'Amuse," by
Victor Hugo.

13. Yes. "The Man Without
a Country."

14. Beethoven's 9th, often called
the "Choral Symphony."

15. Irving Berlin, Harry T.
Burleigh, Stephen Collins
Foster.

16. Weinberger's "Schwanda the
Bagpiper."

17. "Bolero."

18. The violin.

19. Franz Joseph Haydn.

20. In the style of the chapel,
that is, singing unaccom-
panied.

21. Yes, a trilogy by Ottorino
Respighi: "The Fountains
of Rome," the "Pines of
Rome," and "The Festivals
of Rome."

22. John Barbirolli, an Englishman.

23. Sir Arthur Sullivan.

24. "Taps." He whistled the
tune to his bugler while the
Army of the Potomac was
encamped at Harrison's
Landing, Virginia, in 1862.

25. "The Maple Leaf Forever,"
words and music by Alex-
ander Muir.

FAMILIAR SAYINGS QUIZ

1. Keats' "Endymion."

2. Burns, "To a Louse."

3. "Ancient Mariner," by
Coleridge.

4. Pope's "Essay on Criticism."

5. Psalm 107.

6. John P. Curran in a speech
made in Dublin in 1808.

7. "The Sultan of Sula," a
popular musical comedy.

8. Title of a poem by Harriet
Glazebrook.

9. Shakespeare's "Romeo and
Juliet."

10. Samuel Johnson.

11. Remark by Timothy J.
Campbell to President Cleveland.

12. This is a re-wording of Ecclesiastes 1:9.

13. The allusion is to a popular
comic supplement feature by
the cartoonist McManus.

14. The phrase is accredited to
Frank Ward O'Malley.

15. Job XIX:20.

16. Shakespeare's "Julius Caesar," Act 1 Scene 2.
17. Benjamin Disraeli in the House of Commons, January 24, 1860.
18. Letter by Voltaire to Rousseau.
19. Ecclesiastes X:1.
20. Brillat-Savarin.
21. John Babson Lane Soule used it in 1851. Horace Greeley popularized it.
22. William Wordsworth's poem, "Character of the Happy Warrior."
23. James M. Kieran of the New York Times.
24. Probably from one of Swift's letters to Stella, "Now we are even, quoth Steven, when he gave his wife six blows to one."
25. It has been attributed to at least three authors, none of whom claims it.

7. The International Date Line, or the 180° meridian.
8. In their order: white, red, blue.
9. It is solid carbon dioxide.
10. Sierra Nevada Mountains of California.
11. The feeling of being turned around.
12. Theory of Evolution.
13. 1910.
14. About every 76 years.
15. Winter.
16. White hot.
17. Lithosphere.
18. Osmium.
19. No. From petroleum.
20. Back.
21. It is the upper portion of the atmosphere.
22. 93,000,000 miles.
23. Calm area at the center of a tropical cyclone.
24. To measure specific gravity.
25. Yes.

Science Quiz Number 1

1. Yes, there is such a point, known as the blind spot.
2. The Antarctic.
3. Straight.
4. Red lead is used on metals because it helps to prevent formation of rust.
5. Because there is not a complete circuit.
6. Aluminum.

Science Quiz Number 2

1. Earth, Mars, Jupiter, Saturn, Uranus, Neptune.
2. Giraffe.
3. Dmitrii Mendelejef (1834–1907), a Russian chemist.
4. Running water.
5. The minimum tide that occurs during the first and third quarters of the moon's phases.

6. Southern slopes of the Himalaya Mountains in India.
7. Lever, inclined plane, pulley, wheel and axle, screw, wedge.
8. Eighty-eight are recognized today.
9. Carbon dioxide.
10. No. Photographs show it to be sinuous.
11. Oxygen.
12. Diabetes.
13. Laughing gas.
14. Yes for it completely encircles the earth.
15. No, it is curved.
16. Asbestos.
17. Length, weight, time.
18. Mercury.
19. Aluminum.
20. To allow room for the metal to expand.
21. To measure the velocity of the wind.
22. Acid.
23. Just before or just after full moon.
24. Helium.
25. Excessive fear of some object or situation that persists apparently without grounds.

Geography Quiz Number 1

1. The Pacific end is about 27 miles east of the Atlantic end.
2. Louisiana.
3. Guatemala, Honduras, Salvador, Nicaragua, Costa Rica, Panama, British Honduras.
4. Because it is equally distant from the North and South Poles.
5. Oklahoma City had a population of 10,000 under tents by nightfall April 22, 1889, the day it was opened for settlement.
6. Belgium, Germany, Switzerland, Spain, Andorra and Italy.
7. Rome.
8. Christiania. Capital of Norway.
9. Lake Titicaca, which lies between Peru and Bolivia at an altitude of 12,545 feet.
10. Chile. The city is Magallanes, formerly Punta Arenas.
11. The Missouri.
12. Copernicus, (1473–1543).
13. France, at the Italian border.
14. Matthew Fontaine Maury.
15. Brazil.
16. Fishing, automobile industry, Tuskegee Institute, Taj Mahal, wool, winter sports.
17. Larger.
18. Yes, the Maine Desert in the village of Freeport.
19. The principality of Monaco.

20. New Guinea, Peru, Idaho, Switzerland, Turkey, Massachusetts.
21. The Leaning Tower.
22. California.
23. Portugal.
24. Kilauea in Hawaii.
25. India and Afghanistan.

GEOGRAPHY QUIZ NUMBER 2

1. Minnesota.
2. A seaport developed by Poland.
3. Damascus, in Syria.
4. New York, Colorado, California, Virginia, Illinois.
5. A port opened by treaty to foreign trade.
6. Indian Ocean. It is the Bay of Bengal.
7. Los Angeles, California.
8. South America.
9. Colorado and Delaware.
10. Yes, in Norway.
11. Norway, Sweden and Denmark.
12. Union of Soviet Socialist Republics.
13. St. Mark's in Venice.
14. The French Riviera.
15. New Orleans.
16. Asphalt.
17. The Nile.
18. Benares.
19. Chosen.
20. Madeira Islands.
21. Strabo (63 B.C.?–24 A.D.?).

22. A low flat district in Eastern England traversed by innumerable watercourses.
23. Leningrad, Russia, because so many laborers lost their lives in the difficult task of building the city on piles.
24. Diamond Head.
25. In the Canadian Rockies.

ABBREVIATIONS QUIZ

1. Manuscripts.
2. Cambridge.
3. Bachelor of Arts.
4. First class.
5. (Libra) Pound weight.
6. (Ultimo) In the preceding month.
7. (Scilicet) Namely.
8. Confederate States of America.
9. (Dei Gratia) By the Grace of God.
10. Revolutions per minute.
11. Pounds, shillings, pence.
12. (Nota bene) Note well.
13. British Broadcasting Corporation.
14. (Ante meridiem) Before noon.
15. (Videlicet) Namely.
16. Free on Board.
17. (Pour prendre congé) To take leave.
18. (Id est) That is.
19. Aide-de-camp.
20. Philippine Islands.

21. Pennyweight.
22. Society for the Prevention of Cruelty to Children.
23. American Association for the Advancement of Science.
24. Baronet.
25. Canal Zone.

MYTHOLOGY QUIZ

1. Midas.
2. Lares and Penates.
3. Narcissus.
4. Achilles.
5. He was condemned to roll to the top of a hill a huge stone which constantly rolled back again.
6. Fire.
7. Nectar and ambrosia made them immortal.
8. By piling Ossa on Pelion.
9. The ancient Persians.
10. Daedalus.
11. Freya, the Scandinavian goddess of beauty and love.
12. The apple of Discord.
13. By means of her magic she changed men into swine.
14. Charon ferried the dead over the River Styx, Chiron was a centaur famous for knowledge of medicine.
15. Niobe.
16. Turned into stone every living thing that saw it.
17. Daughter of the moon in North American Indian mythology.
18. Gold and silver palace of Odin where he received the souls of heroes slain in battle.
19. Castor and Pollux.
20. By a thread which Ariadne had given him.
21. Cupid.
22. Cadmus.
23. A wooden horse.
24. Heifer.
25. He had two faces looking in opposite directions.

AMERICAN HISTORY QUIZ NUMBER 1

1. Israel Putnam.
2. William Penn's treaty with the Indians.
3. Rhode Island with Newport and Providence; Connecticut with Hartford and New Haven; Oklahoma with Guthrie and Oklahoma City.
4. South Carolina, December 20, 1860.
5. Massachusetts Bay Colony exiled Roger Williams in 1636.
6. He was killed in a duel with Aaron Burr, fought in Weehawken, N. J., 1804.
7. Santa Anna.
8. Plains of Abraham, Quebec, 1759. Wolfe (Br.) Montcalm (Fr.).

9. Fort Sumter, April, 1861.
10. William Pitt, Edmund Burke, Charles James Fox.
11. Charles C. Pinckney.
12. Massachusetts bought the claims of the Gorges heirs to the State of Maine in 1677 for about 1250 English pounds.
13. War of 1812.
14. Stephen A. Douglas.
15. General Henry Lee.
16. Wyoming in 1869.
17. Tennessee.
18. The Stamp Act was so called by Benjamin Franklin.
19. Roanoke Island, North Carolina.
20. From Amerigo Vespucci.
21. Jefferson Davis.
22. Trent Affair.
23. Harding.
24. The *Maine*.
25. Robert E. Lee.

AMERICAN HISTORY QUIZ
NUMBER 2

1. Yes, in what is now Tennessee. It was organized in 1784.
2. "Don't fire until you see the whites of their eyes."
3. Kentucky.
4. Millard Fillmore.
5. General Winfield Scott.
6. Daniel Webster.
7. John Paul Jones.

8. In 1867, from Russia.
9. Gettysburg, 1863.
10. Benjamin Franklin.
11. Andrew Jackson.
12. John Hay.
13. Leif Ericson.
14. Brigadier General Frederick Funston.
15. Benjamin Franklin, after signing the Declaration of Independence.
16. Andrew Jackson's. On becoming President, he rewarded his supporters, declaring that, "to the victors belong the spoils."
17. Meriwether Lewis.
18. Major Pitcairn to the Minute Men at Lexington, Massachusetts, in 1775.
19. The Peale Family.
20. Ulysses S. Grant.
21. Clay, Webster and Calhoun.
22. Commodore George Dewey.
23. Charles Bonaparte.
24. Underground railway.
25. The last expedition against the Florida Indians to force them out of the State.

RADIO QUIZ

1. For commercial programs between 7:00 and 10:30 P.M.
2. Milton T. Cross, Alwyn Bach, David Ross, James

Wallington, Alois Havrilla, John Holbrook.

3. W and K.
4. Samuel L. Rothafel.
5. California and New York.
6. Uncle Don, National Farm and Home Hour, Orphan Annie, Amos 'n' Andy.
7. "Carefree," by Charles Henderson and Pat Ballard.
8. Programs that are recorded on phonograph records.
9. Edgar Bergen.
10. President Harding in 1923.
11. Amos.
12. Thirteen weeks.
13. Cincinnati, Ohio, Station WLW.
14. Chase and Sanborn.
15. It simply means distant stations.
16. The nautical term was adopted because radio operators on vessels first began to keep such a record.
17. Eddie Cantor.
18. Sponsored and sustaining.
19. Seth Parker.
20. American Society of Composers, Authors and Publishers.
21. Kathryn Cravens.
22. Deanna Durbin.
23. Walt Disney for Micky Mouse.
24. Niagara Falls.
25. Al Jolson.

MOTION PICTURE QUIZ

1. Three years.
2. 283,000.
3. Luise Rainer.
4. "Great American Train Robbery" produced in 1903.
5. They signify that he belongs to the American Society of Cinematographers.
6. Myrna Loy.
7. "Room Service."
8. Pathé in 1910.
9. W. C. Fields.
10. Better known as Paulette Goddard, Gail Patrick and Gene Raymond.
11. Katherine Hepburn.
12. Frederic March.
13. Grace George.
14. London, England.
15. "Mr. Deeds Goes to Town."
16. Pearl White.
17. Robert Taylor's.
18. Westerns.
19. D. W. Griffith is credited with their introduction.
20. Hungary.
21. Sessue Hayakawa.
22. Colorado School of Mines.
23. It was named for an estate in England.
24. Dorothy Arzner.
25. No—Culver City, California.

MATHEMATICS QUIZ

1. 2, 3, 5, 7, 11, 13, 17, 19, 23.
2. Greatest Common Divisor

and Least Common Multiple.

3. One in which the two angles at the base are equal.
4. 360.
5. John Napier, a Scottish mathematician.
6. One, followed by thirty-nine ciphers.
7. Tore.
8. Rule for finding fourth term of a proportion where three are given.
9. A number, the sum of whose divisors is equal to the number.
10. No.
11. Earth measurement.
12. Only one, length.
13. Area of a circle.
14. CM.
15. The meter, equivalent to 39.37 inches.
16. Five.
17. The volume required to cover one acre to the depth of one foot.
18. That part of a number which will divide the number without remainder.
19. Pons Asinorum, Euclid Book 1, Prop. V.
20. Median.
21. A Russian measure of distance equal to two-thirds of a mile.
22. Greeks and Romans.
23. Second.

24. In India.
25. Half base x perpendicular height; base x half perpendicular height.

DRAMA QUIZ

1. Cyrano de Bergerac.
2. Guthrie McClintic.
3. Because at one time the walls were painted green to relieve eyes of players affected by the glare of stage lights.
4. Ethel Barrymore.
5. Noel Coward.
6. Japanese symbolic and traditional drama.
7. Thespis, sixth century B.C. is the reputed founder of Greek tragedy.
8. "Abie's Irish Rose," "Lightnin'," "Tobacco Road," "The Bat," "The Ladder," "The First Year," "Seventh Heaven," "Peg O' My Heart," "East is West," "Irene," "Children's Hour," "Trip to Chinatown," "Rain," "The Green Pastures," "Broadway."
9. Maude Adams.
10. Lily Langtry. She was born on the island of Jersey, and Millais so named a portrait of her.
11. "Macbeth."
12. Blythe.
13. Beneath the Shakespeare

monument in Westminster Abbey.
14. Closet dramas.
15. Time, place, location.
16. Anne Nichols.
17. Sarah Kemble Siddons.
18. Richard Mansfield.
19. Charles Chaplin and Harpo Marx.
20. The late Will Rogers.
21. Otis Skinner.
22. Orson Welles of the Mercury Theatre productions.
23. The comedians George Burns and Jack Benny.
24. David Belasco.
25. "Abraham Lincoln," written by John Drinkwater.

NEWSPAPER QUIZ

1. William Randolph Hearst.
2. Eleanor Patterson, publisher of the *Washington Herald* and *Times*.
3. Associated Press.
4. Henry Watterson, publisher of the *Louisville Courier-Journal*.
5. Editor and Publisher.
6. Dorothy Dix.
7. Charles B. Driscoll.
8. Arthur Brisbane.
9. (1) George McManus; (2) James Swinnerton; (3) George Herriman.
10. *The Gentlemen's Magazine* founded in London 1731.

11. They are publishers' checks on distribution channels.
12. *Liberty Magazine.*
13. On an average day the *Times* has about 150,000 words of reading matter.
14. Woman writer of sentimental news articles.
15. *The Stars and Stripes.*
16. *The News,* New York City.
17. A daily paper of small format.
18. It was the first woman's magazine in this country.
19. Audit Bureau of Circulation.
20. The late Thomas A. Edison.
21. The signature of the writer.
22. St. Petersburg (Florida) *Independent.*
23. *London Times.*
24. Ulster County Gazette, containing the account of Washington's funeral.
25. To the Roman Empire.

LAW QUIZ

1. Common law is unwritten law, statutory law depends upon statutes.
2. The doing of a lawful act in an unlawful manner.
3. Quebec.
4. Subpoena.
5. The Bible.
6. Person under legal age, which usually is 21.

7. Barratry.
8. The interest in the estate of a deceased husband which the law gives to his widow during her lifetime.
9. Charles Evans Hughes.
10. The Volstead Act was a Federal law passed by Congress to enforce the 18th Amendment to the Constitution.
11. No.
12. Defense of the Realm Act.
13. Riparian Rights.
14. The Constitution.
15. Twenty-eight years, renewable for a further 28 years.
16. Without leaving a will.
17. Colony of New Haven, about 1640.
18. One providing that a wife may remarry without formality of divorce after the husband has been absent a specified number of years.
19. A celebrated body of Roman laws on twelve bronze tables.
20. From the practice of obliging citizens to cover their fires each night.
21. Senator Caleb H. Baumes of New York.
22. These rights include not only the rights over physical property but also those of life, liberty and reputation.
23. In the Tariff Act of June 6, 1872, a comma placed between fruit and trees caused both to be admitted duty free when it was intended to place "fruit trees" on the free list.
24. 24,902 from 1789–1937.
25. Any wrongful act (not involving a breach of contract) for which a civil action may be brought.

TRAVEL QUIZ

1. Carlsbad Caverns.
2. Atlantic City, New Jersey.
3. Metro.
4. Virginia; Yellowstone Park; New York State; California (on the Nevada boundary).
5. Yes, Delhi, India.
6. Quebec, Canada.
7. Virginia and North Carolina.
8. United Fruit Company.
9. The Bermudas.
10. Chicago.
11. Oregon; Maine; Massachusetts; Yosemite National Park (California).
12. England, France, Germany, Switzerland and Italy.
13. The United States-Canadian border.
14. Florence.
15. (1) London; (2) Berlin; (3) Vienna.
16. Egypt.

17. Scotland.
18. The Lido.
19. Ireland.
20. Midnight Sun.
21. *Queen Mary* (British); *Normandie* (French).
22. It is said to have been so named by Sir Francis Drake.
23. In a gondola.
24. Jaipur, India, is so called.
25. Italian Line.

WORLD WAR QUIZ

1. General Pershing.
2. Yes, in the autumn of 1914 they came within fifteen miles of Paris.
3. Doughboys, Tommies, Poilus.
4. October 21, 1917, when the First Division entered the Luneville Section near Nancy.
5. "Tipperary."
6. Sergeant Alvin York.
7. Blighty.
8. General Foch.
9. Zero hour.
10. Yes, the most important was the Battle of Tannenberg or the Masurian Lakes, September 1, 1914.
11. Romanov, Hapsburg and Hohenzollern.
12. Germany lost it to France.
13. H. G. Wells.
14. No.
15. April 6; 1917.
16. Chateau-Thierry, Saint Mihiel, Meuse-Argonne.
17. In a message to Congress on January 8, 1918.
18. Yes, on November 9, 1918.
19. He was Director of the Committee on Public Information.
20. The Second Battalion of the 308th Infantry, 77th Division A.E.F., which was under the command of Major Charles White Whittlesey, held out for five days and nights, October 2–7, 1918, entirely cut off from all communication with its own forces and surrounded by the enemy.
21. President Wilson used it in a speech at Philadelphia, May 10, 1915, three days after the Lusitania was torpedoed (May 7, 1915).
22. 8,461,595 dead, 21,099,935 wounded.
23. President Wilson used the phrase in his message delivered to Congress, April 2, 1917.
24. She was shot by a French firing squad October 15, 1917.
25. The bugles sounded "cease firing" at 11 A.M., November 11, 1918.

BUSINESS QUIZ

1. Furniture. The Val Kill Shop at Hyde Park, New York.
2. Aaron Montgomery Ward.
3. Gordon Selfridge.
4. Yes, the American Telephone and Telegraph Company.
5. Two, voluntary and involuntary.
6. Silent partner.
7. Great Atlantic and Pacific Tea Company.
8. One that contains daily reminders in follow-up correspondence.
9. Secretary.
10. Marshall Field.
11. No, it was imported from Paris more than a century ago.
12. Shoes.
13. Clarence Saunders.
14. Statistician.
15. Dun and Bradstreet.
16. Abraham Lincoln. His name was Robert Lincoln.
17. Rubber goods, shoes, furniture, salt, meat packing, steel.
18. Industrial revolution.
19. Formulation of mortality tables.
20. New York.
21. Twelve months counted as a year in financial operations.
22. Business cycle.
23. Middleman.
24. Cost insurance and freight; errors and omissions excepted.
25. (1) Department store; (2) paint manufacture; (3) soaps and cosmetics; (4) marine insurance.

AERONAUTICS QUIZ

1. Juan de la Cierva.
2. Wiley Post.
3. 1927.
4. No, but he made the first solo flight across that ocean.
5. Wilbur and Orville Wright.
6. When opened, it has an umbrella spread of 24 feet.
7. General Italo Balbo.
8. Dr. Augusti Piccard, May 27, 1931.
9. Louis Bleriot, of France.
10. The Bureau of Air Commerce, Department of Commerce.
11. An airplane designed to rise from and alight on either land or water.
12. Fuselage.
13. A shelter for housing airplanes.
14. To fly without engine power and without loss of altitude.
15. Amelia Earhart.
16. Calbraith Rodgers left New York September 17, 1911

with a Wright biplane. After 49 days of mishaps and delays he landed at Pasadena, California, November 5th.

17. Hydrogen.
18. *Shenandoah, Akron, Macon.*
19. Anne Morrow.
20. Pensacola, Florida.
21. At Kitty Hawk, North Carolina. The date was December 17, 1903, and the flight lasted twelve seconds.
22. The first balloon ascension in America took place at Philadelphia, January 9, 1793, when Blanchard, Europe's leading balloonist, made a flight of 45 minutes. The spectacle was witnessed by President Washington.
23. Sir Charles Kingsford-Smith's.
24. Dr. Hugo Eckener.
25. The United States.

FESTIVALS AND HOLIDAYS QUIZ

1. Arbor Day. It is celebrated in most states either in April or May, and was first appointed in Nebraska in 1872.
2. Ash Wednesday.
3. Jubilee. Originally it was a plenary indulgence proclaimed by the Pope every 25 years, or during a time of stress or rejoicing. The first jubilee on record is that of 1300, ordered by Boniface VIII.
4. Japan.
5. Important days in the Church calendar were marked with a red letter.
6. Miss Anna Jarvis of Philadelphia. We celebrate the day on the second Sunday in May.
7. A leave of absence; from the custom of the Israelites to leave their fields and vineyards at rest every seventh year.
8. Pasadena, California, January 1.
9. Chinese.
10. The discovery of the plot to blow up Parliament by Guy Fawkes in 1605. It is called Guy Fawkes Day.
11. Manifestation. Epiphany originally was celebrated on January 6 to commemorate the baptism of Christ, but since the 5th century it commemorates the coming of the Magi as the occasion of the first manifestation of Christ to the Gentiles.
12. Carnival, derived from "carne vale."
13. Ground Hog Day. Candlemas, celebrated on February 2, commemorates the

presentation of Christ in the temple.

14. May 1st.
15. St. John, the Baptist (June 24).
16. Popularly the period between Christmas and Epiphany. Originally the old pagan festival of the winter solstice was celebrated at this time. Twelfth Night, January 6th, the feast of Epiphany concluded the Medieval Christmas festivities.
17. Saint Catherine's Day, November 25.
18. Rosh Hashanah, New Year. It occurs on the first and second day of Tishri, the seventh month of the Jewish calendar.
19. China.
20. Fall of the Bastille in 1789. It is celebrated on July 14th.
21. Annual national congress to encourage Welsh music and literature. The institution goes back at least to the 12th century.
22. Bishop of Winchester, England, in the 9th Century. Saint Suretin's Day is celebrated on July 15th. According to popular tradition if it rains on that day it will continue to rain for 40 days.
23. Mothering Sunday, fourth Sunday in Lent. The cus-

tom is to visit one's mother with a gift offering.

24. Departure of the Steamship Savannah in 1819.
25. Dominion Day, July 1st.

EDUCATION QUIZ

1. Boston, Mass.
2. Friedrich Wilhelm Froebel (1782–1852).
3. The University of San Marcos in Lima, Peru, founded in 1551.
4. Because the close of the school period marks the commencement of life's activities.
5. Bennington College, Vermont.
6. Colonial schools established by women (dames) in their homes.
7. As early as 1117 there are notices of continental scholars lecturing at Oxford, and it was already a center of learning in 1185.
8. One in which students study part time and work part time. An example is Antioch, in Ohio.
9. Since 1918 such laws have existed in all the States.
10. Confucius.
11. University in Paris. It originated in 1257, when Louis IX's chaplain, Robert de Sorbon established a house

for poor theological students. It is now the seat for the public courses of the University of Paris.

12. Question and answer.

13. Peter Abelard. (1079–1142)

14. Binet-Simon. After Alfred Binet (1857–1911) and Theodore Simon, two French psychologists.

15. Washington and Lee.

16. Johann Heinrich Pestalozzi (1746–1827).

17. An assigned course of study.

18. Columbia University, New York, with 31,898.

19. Denmark .1, Sweden .29, Scotland .29.

20. Cecil J. Rhodes.

21. University of Virginia at Charlottesville, which he founded.

22. Five-Foot Shelf of Books.

23. Originator of a well-known system of calisthenics. François (1811–1871) was a French teacher of dramatic and musical expression.

24. A system was invented by Timothy Bright during Queen Elizabeth's reign.

25. West Point, New York.

FINANCE QUIZ

1. Leiter corner 1898; Patten corner 1909.

2. No. A security is said to be *at par* when the market price equals the par value, or price at which it was issued.

3. From the practice of buying and selling securities on the curbstone or in the middle of the street.

4. Slang term for a shilling.

5. The average life is less than six months.

6. Decimal system.

7. Due bill.

8. Miscellaneous securities of doubtful speculative value.

9. The Bible describes Joseph's corner of the grain in Egypt.

10. 1907.

11. William Jennings Bryan.

12. Bank of North America in Philadelphia.

13. The Roman Emperor Augustus.

14. Long term.

15. It is the center of banking transactions in London.

16. Rothschild.

17. No, a private institution.

18. Wall Street.

19. Extension of time for meeting financial obligations.

20. Sir Basil Zaharoff.

21. Basel, Switzerland.

22. Hungary.

23. William Gibbs McAdoo.

24. J. P. Morgan.

25. Irish dividend.

Etiquette Quiz

1. The third.
2. Fifteen to twenty minutes.
3. No, the surname should be added to the title.
4. It is not.
5. The prospective bridegroom.
6. Bread, crackers, olives, celery, radishes, nuts, candy, raw fruits, small pickles and corn on the cob.
7. Thomas Jefferson.
8. No, he should walk on the outside, or street side.
9. No.
10. The best man.
11. No.
12. No, to her escort.
13. No, it is a compliment to the hostess or cook to eat everything on the plate.
14. Yes.
15. Never.
16. Two to four weeks before the date.
17. Yes, it is essential and its omission is a social error.
18. Address it to both husband and wife.
19. She may do so.
20. Madam President is the correct title.
21. No, not until he leaves school.
22. No. Mr. Brown, unless he is a Doctor of Divinity, when Dr. Brown is used.
23. Just the same as when her husband was living.
24. No, it is not considered good taste.
25. Remove them.

Curious Customs Quiz

1. It is a corruption of "God be with you."
2. Eggs are the symbol of resurrection.
3. Christmas.
4. In England. Such signs were used in London long before they came to America.
5. Medici family of Italy. Their arms consisted of three balls.
6. Ceremony aboard ship when crossing the Equator.
7. In 1659 it was unlawful in Massachusetts to have a Merry Christmas.
8. The ability to get what you want by cajolery.
9. According to some authorities in ancient Mesopotamia.
10. It was not unknown in the Old World and is mentioned by Herodotus.
11. The custom started in Europe with the idea of avoiding the window tax and at the same time giving an appearance of affluence.
12. On the last day of the year, children go about singing,

and receive a dole, usually of cakes.

13. Emblem or representation of the clan or family among the West Coast Indians of North America.

14. In India. This custom, now nearly obsolete, called for the faithful widow to cremate herself on the funeral pyre of her husband.

15. Bologna, Italy.

16. Saint Patrick.

17. The addition of the day was to ensure completion of the full year term.

18. Napoleon.

19. From Saint Nicholas, a patron saint of children.

20. China.

21. Elizabeth of England.

22. Pope Innocent IV bestowed them on the secular cardinals as a symbol of their readiness to shed their blood for Christ and Church.

23. A spoon, whose handle bears a small figure of an Apostle.

24. Something old, something new, something borrowed, something blue.

25. The queue or pigtail.

ARMY AND NAVY QUIZ

1. U.S.S.R. (Russia).

2. The Secretary of the Navy, with the approval of the President.

3. Busby.

4. Commodore Esek Hopkins. (1718–1802)

5. Four. The Battle Force, Scouting Force, Submarine Force and Base Force.

6. German. The term comes from the Turkish word meaning youth, and was applied to Tartar lancers. First introduced into European armies during the Turkish wars in Poland.

7. Iceland.

8. At the age of nine.

9. Yes, he is a commissioned officer below the rank of captain.

10. Croix de Guerre.

11. The thirteen original States.

12. Originally they had quarters amidships.

13. Yes, all major countries except the United States and the British Empire.

14. They are: Battle of Marathon, 490 B.C.; Syracuse, 413 B.C.; Arminius over Rome, 9 A.D.; Hastings, 1066; Orleans, 1429; Spanish Armada, 1588; Blenheim, 1704; Pultowa, 1709; Saratoga, 1777; Valmy, 1792; Waterloo, 1815; Gettysburg, 1863;

Manila, 1898; Marne, 1914; Verdun, 1916.

15. Bersaglieri, a corps of infantry in the Italian Army.
16. Marines.
17. Sidi-bel-Abbes, Algeria.
18. Napoleon.
19. Tactics.
20. April 6.
21. Fish.
22. Medical Corps.
23. Admiral William S. Sims.
24. 65.51 pounds.
25. Company.

TRANSPORTATION QUIZ

1. Common carrier.
2. A merchant sailing vessel.
3. *Natchez*. The *Robert E. Lee* won.
4. Ten to twelve hours, without delays.
5. Sir Samuel Cunard. (1787–1865)
6. The Erie Canal.
7. None, it is a sea level canal.
8. Traffic is about evenly divided.
9. Because of the long overhanging prow and sharp lines.
10. St. Mary's Canal. It forms a navigable connection between lakes Superior and Huron.
11. Plimsoll Line.
12. The War Trail of the

Six Nations extended from Chautauqua N. Y. to Georgia.
13. 11,000 miles.
14. *The Great Republic.* 4555 tons. Launched by Donald McKay Oct. 4th, 1853.
15. It crosses from the Colorado River to the irrigated area of the Imperial Valley.
16. U. S. Highway #1 in the vicinity of New York City.
17. Sir John Macadam.
18. Glacier National Park, Montana.
19. Brigade of cars.
20. Masters of Transportation.
21. The first actual railway in the U.S. was the "Granite Railroad" constructed by Gridley Grant in 1826 to carry blocks of granite from Quincy, Mass. to the Bunker Hill Monument.
22. *The Pioneer,* bought at second-hand by the line, which afterwards became the Chicago and Northwestern. Its first trip was in 1848.
23. *The Sandusky,* a locomotive of the Mad River and Lake Erie Railroad in Ohio in 1837.
24. Two dollars for an overnight berth.
25. The Chicago and Alton placed the first regular din-

ing car, *the Delmonico,* in service in 1868.

FLAG QUIZ

1. In the Old National Museum, Washington, D. C.
2. None. No star in the flag represents any given State.
3. Flag, color, standard, ensign.
4. It may not.
5. A salute from the French fleet under Admiral Piquet in 1778.
6. Six.
7. The church pennant.
8. June 14, 1777.
9. Union Jack of Great Britain. They are the crosses of St. George, St. Andrew and St. Patrick.
10. Tricolor of France.
11. Dannebrog of Denmark dating from 1219.
12. That of Liberia.
13. July 4, 1912, when the last of the 48 states entered the union.
14. Mississippi.
15. Never, except to cover a coffin.
16. Maryland. It bears the Calvert arms.
17. Ordinarily a flat button. Army flag poles have a spearhead, the President's flag, an eagle.

18. Military colors.
19. Pennants.
20. Run to the top and then lowered to half-staff.
21. Bunting.
22. Blood red flag with revolution; black flag with pirates.
23. That of Japan.
24. Union of England, Scotland and Ireland.
25. That of Transvaal, Union of South Africa.

SLANG QUIZ

1. To be moved by personal interests.
2. Acknowledge defeat.
3. To speak in plain terms.
4. Insincere grief.
5. Intrude.
6. To take what is coming to you.
7. To do one's full duty.
8. Reprimand or reprove.
9. Overcome restraint.
10. To die.
11. Give away a secret.
12. To the bottom of the ocean. Sailors' term for drowning.
13. Think hard, puzzle.
14. To be a coward.
15. Mediocre.
16. Make your own way, mind your own business.
17. Take the prize.
18. A bad character.

19. To be possessed with a persistent or fixed idea.
20. To deceive or mislead.
21. On credit.
22. A foolish undertaking.
23. To be two-faced. To waver.
24. Born to luxury and wealth.
25. To be on the wrong scent or course.

AMERICANA QUIZ

1. Detroit, Michigan.
2. September 7, 1776, by the Continental Congress.
3. Alaska and Hawaii.
4. Texas.
5. No, they must be white.
6. Reno.
7. The Sequoia.
8. Massachusetts.
9. Yes, one, in Provincetown, Massachusetts.
10. The late Huey Long.
11. The White House.
12. Yes, in Maryland and Delaware.
13. Kentucky.
14. Republican partisans during the Presidential campaign of 1860 who marched wearing uniforms and wide-awake hats.
15. President Grover Cleveland.
16. Virgin Islands.
17. Thirty-one.
18. Buchanan.
19. Tyler.

20. Theodore Roosevelt (forty-two).
21. William Henry Harrison.
22. He was one who upon payment of a bounty enlisted in the army and afterward deserted from the service.
23. January 20, 1937.
24. Grover Cleveland.
25. Franklin Pierce.

FIRST THINGS QUIZ

1. Virginia, 1612.
2. Pennsylvania *Packet and General Advertiser,* Philadelphia, 1784.
3. Los Angeles, California.
4. Benjamin Franklin, in 1784.
5. Home Insurance Company Building, Chicago.
6. The *Columbia,* in 1787.
7. He made the first linotype machine in 1885.
8. George Westinghouse.
9. John Adams.
10. During an attack on Fort Sumter, 1861.
11. It was the first steamboat on the Great Lakes.
12. Virginia Dare. Born in 1587.
13. It was first isolated in 1838 by scientists Davy and Wohler.
14. Williamsburg, Virginia, about 1718.

15. They constituted the first public telegraph message.
16. Benjamin Symmes bequeathed 250 acres of land and eight milk cows to found a free school in Elizabeth County, Virginia. That was in 1634.
17. George IV of England.
18. Frances Perkins.
19. Probably in Egypt.
20. Louis Napoleon, 1848.
21. Ellen Louise Axson.
22. Nellie Bly.
23. Grotius. (De Groot) He was a Dutch jurist who lived from 1583 to 1645.
24. Eli Whitney in 1793.
25. Gold was first discovered.

Foods Quiz

1. Onions, garlic, shallots, chives.
2. Yes, in Arkansas, Louisiana, Texas, California and Missouri.
3. A mass of microscopic living plants.
4. Cole slaw.
5. From a hotel known as the Porter House in Sandusky, Ohio.
6. Milk.
7. Rice.
8. Six seconds.
9. China.

10. Pancreas or thymus gland of calf or other animal.
11. Earl of Sandwich.
12. Abyssinia.
13. No, it is not a true nut, but belongs to the same family as the pea and bean.
14. Salt water fish and shell fish.
15. 196.
16. Pumpkin, squash, cucumber, melon.
17. Planked steak.
18. Bread.
19. There are no foods that are especially brain foods. Any food that nourishes the body nourishes all parts.
20. Milk.
21. Edward VII. Chicken à la king.
22. Salmon.
23. Soy bean.
24. Sago.
25. Department of Agriculture.

Foreign Words and Phrases Quiz

1. The human species to which man belongs.
2. We praise Thee, O God (Latin).
3. Hotel landlord (French).
4. In proportion (Latin).
5. Not of sound mind (Latin).
6. I serve (German).
7. Face to face; confidential

with only two persons concerned. (French).

8. From the books or library of. (Latin).

9. Terrible child or one who makes embarrassing remarks (French).

10. A cause for war (Latin).

11. World pain (German).

12. Literally 10,000 years. Used in the spirit of "Hurrah, Live forever." (Japanese).

13. My dear friend (Spanish).

14. Nobility imposes obligations (French).

15. High treason (French).

16. Wonderful to relate (Latin).

17. A substitute (Latin).

18. Say nothing but good of the dead (Latin).

19. The desire to wander (German).

20. Who knows (Spanish).

21. Self-government (Hindu).

22. Day of wrath, Judgment Day (Latin).

23. Gilded youth (French).

24. I have found it (Greek).

25. Therefore, let us rejoice (Latin).

SUPERSTITIONS QUIZ

1. Because the ancient Greeks and Romans used salt in their sacrifices, and to spill it was an ill omen.

2. Because the Egyptian cat-headed goddess Pasht was so endowed.

3. A mascot or a charm.

4. Russia.

5. The last line.

6. The Basilisk.

7. No.

8. Open side up.

9. Fair weather.

10. Opal.

11. Siam.

12. Because its four leaves are in the shape of a cross.

13. "Rainbow in morning, shepherds take warning."

14. An imaginary female being.

15. To drop a coin into it ensures a traveler's safe return to Rome.

16. Water in its eye.

17. No.

18. No, it does not.

19. The caul or veil is supposed to give second sight, and immunity from drowning.

20. An onion tied about the wrist.

21. The right shoe.

22. Wednesday.

23. The reflection was thought to be a part of the soul and to break the substance on which it was reflected was to injure the soul itself.

24. No. They actually grow smaller (through action of the elements).

25. A white or bright hued plume is supposed to be "good medicine."

Advertising Slogans Quiz

1. In the New York *Times*.
2. The Hamilton.
3. Smokers of Marlboro Cigarettes.
4. Makers of Fleischmann's yeast.
5. When traveling on the C & O.
6. Reading Dr. Eliot's Five-Foot Shelf of Books.
7. Makers of Squibb's toothpaste.
8. Maxwell House coffee.
9. Roth Memory Course.
10. Camels.
11. Morton's salt.
12. Chase and Sanborn's coffee.
13. Packard Motors.
14. Steinway.
15. Carnation.
16. Sherwin-Williams paint.
17. Fisk Tire Company.
18. Dr. Lyons' tooth powder.
19. Castoria.
20. Bon Ami.
21. By using Palmolive soap.
22. Lifebuoy soap.
23. Gold Medal flour.
24. Makers of Fels naphtha soap.
25. Schlitz beer.

Ships and Navigation Quiz

1. *Niña, Pinta, Santa Maria.*
2. The *Savannah.*
3. The *Britannia.*
4. She was sold for junk in 1937.
5. *Normandie* and *Queen Mary.*
6. An American mathematician (1773–1838) whose book on navigation enabled the American merchant marine to outsail all competitors.
7. Crew.
8. *Morro Castle.*
9. From about 10 to 13 knots an hour.
10. The *I'm Alone.*
11. An instrument for determining a ship's position at sea.
12. In 1870. On the Mississippi River.
13. At the Navy Yard, Boston, Massachusetts.
14. *Vaterland.*
15. Lloyd's of London, England.
16. Cabin class, second class and third class.
17. A tramp vessel.
18. The *Thomas W. Lawson.*
19. No.
20. The *U. S. S. Maine.*
21. The *Monitor* and the *Merrimac.*
22. The *Mayflower.*
23. Admiral Farragut.
24. None.
25. The ship's log.

RELIGION QUIZ

1. A tree representing the genealogy of Jesus Christ from the root of Jesse.
2. David.
3. Cathedral of St. John the Divine.
4. Kindness, uprightness, decorum, wisdom, truth.
5. March 29, 1463, the day of the Battle of Towton when more than 37,000 Englishmen were slain.
6. Cardinals are appointed for life.
7. Oxford Group Movement.
8. A person who was hired to eat the sins of one who had just died.
9. Buddha.
10. Agnosticism is a declaration of not having found a basis for belief; Atheism is avowed disbelief.
11. Brahma.
12. Heinrich Graetz.
13. The ancient native religion of Japan.
14. Yes, they came in 1735 as spiritual advisers to General Oglethorpe's colony in Georgia.
15. Martin Luther.
16. It is a Greek word meaning universal.
17. Christian Science, founded by Mary Baker Eddy.
18. The compilation of oral law of the Jews, the accepted authority for Orthodox Jews.
19. Quakers.
20. Mohammedan crier of the hour of prayer.
21. That which teaches the doctrine of one God.
22. At Methodist and other revivals, the bench set aside for those who had repented of their sins and wished to be re-admitted to the church.
23. Wars of the French Government against the Huguenots (1562–98).
24. Hegira.
25. Tonsure.

COIN QUIZ

1. The mint at Philadelphia.
2. Front.
3. Lydia, in Asia Minor.
4. Germany.
5. Cambist.
6. England. It is twenty-one shillings.
7. To reduce in purity or value as by adding alloy.
8. To detect possible loss of weight caused by scraping the edges.
9. Denver or San Francisco Mints.
10. India.
11. One used as a kind of pass by slaves in escaping by the

so-called underground rail-road.

12. Mills are not coined although listed as currency.
13. From the foundation of the republic.
14. Yes, on the island of Yap.
15. Specie.
16. Only four.
17. Chinese, around 1000 A.D.
18. Copper.
19. Red-headed woodpecker.
20. 1864.
21. Rarity and condition.
22. Poland.
23. Uncoined gold or silver.
24. Polish the coin. If it is yellowish it is brass, if reddish it is copper.
25. Yes, gold coins known as angels were in use in England from 1460–1625.

STAMP QUIZ

1. Yes, George Washington by France in 1927, and by Poland in 1932.
2. Stamps sold at a dollar each to create a special fund known as Migratory Bird Conservation Fund.
3. Armenia.
4. One which is embossed on an envelope but not inked, and therefore colorless.
5. Only one, issued by Italy in 1923.
6. President Franklin D. Roosevelt and the late King George V of England.
7. Dr. Zamenhof, author of Esperanto, by Russia in 1927.
8. Loving exemption from tax (Greek).
9. British Guiana one-cent magenta stamp.
10. The envelope to which a stamp is attached.
11. Spitzbergen.
12. Benjamin Franklin's.
13. Pony Express. Stage Coach.
14. England.
15. Philatelist.
16. Those no longer valid for postage.
17. It means air (air mail).
18. Dead Letter Office.
19. British Consular Mail.
20. Mexico, to raise funds to combat ravages of the grasshopper.
21. Sir Rowland Hill. (1795–1879)
22. Occupied Enemy Territory and French Military Occupation.
23. British and colonial stamps with portrait of Queen Victoria.
24. Northern Mongolia.
25. Bureau of Printing and Engraving in Washington, D. C.

GENEALOGY QUIZ

1. Not in the modern sense. All members of a large tribe may be called brothers, sons, fathers and the like, when, in the modern sense, the relation would be very remote.

2. Probably none. Even the greatest European houses rise only after the Dark Ages.

3. It was especially active in Queen Elizabeth's reign.

4. Cross flory.

5. No, they are not.

6. One divided into four equal parts by a cross.

7. It was the ornament on the upper part of the helmet.

8. By the word or, and by dots or points.

9. Achievement.

10. Records of land transfer from one generation to the next.

11. Not wholly, they are seldom regarded as good legal evidence.

12. Because he wore a dolphin as his emblem.

13. Not unless granted by the English. In early Irish history there were no coats-of-arms.

14. Usually not.

15. No, they were a later invention.

16. It is the figure such as an animal or bird which appears above the coat-of-arms.

17. Younger sons place a small mark on the family shield to indicate departure from the main line of descent. It may take various forms such as a bird, a beast, etc.

18. The badge usually is of earlier origin. It may be taken from the coat-of-arms. If a shield has a design of several lions, the lion may be termed the badge. The white rose of York and the red rose of Lancaster are famous badges; also the three ostrich plumes of the Prince of Wales.

19. It is a coat showing quarterings. Each of four quarters of the shield may show the arms of a branch of a family and each quarter may be quartered indefinitely.

20. Not blank colors or metals, but there are examples of fur with no design or figure super-imposed.

21. Seldom, the idea is an invention of novelists.

22. Richard I.

23. Scotland.

24. Duke of Norfolk.

25. Official visits by the King-at-Arms or other heraldic officer to examine into pedi-

grees and claims to bear arms.

1. Sir Francis Drake's.
2. Theodore Roosevelt.
3. Carl Akeley.
4. In the Antarctic, on the edge of the Ross Barrier.
5. A bathysphere.
6. General Adolphus Greely.
7. Delia J. Akeley, Mary L. J. Akeley, Osa Johnson, Grace Thompson Seton.
8. No, he went through the Straits of Magellan.
9. Admiral Byrd on his second expedition to the Antarctic.
10. Henry Hudson.
11. New York City.
12. It is not known. He disappeared while in search of the *Italia*.
13. Yes, by Sir Hubert Wilkins.
14. De Soto.
15. Fountain of Youth.
16. Fifteenth and Sixteenth Centuries.
17. Matthew Henson who accompanied Peary to the North Pole.
18. Captain James Cook.
19. Marco Polo.
20. Admiral Peary.
21. Salomon Auguste Andrée.
22. Sir Francis Drake.
23. A northwest passage.

24. Bernard P. Hubbard.
25. Pemmican.

1. 98.8°
2. All blood goes in and out of the heart once every minute.
3. Hippocrates.
4. Protoplasm.
5. Thirty.
6. Nosology.
7. Ganglion is a group of nerve cells; gangrene is the death of part of the body.
8. Father Damien.
9. Typhus.
10. No, it does not.
11. The cause of colds has not yet been isolated.
12. (1) Allergy; (2) energy.
13. Well born.
14. It is carried by rats and transmitted to man by the flea.
15. Lying down.
16. No, a light straw color.
17. Approximately 3500.
18. From 30 to 40.
19. The femur. (thigh bone)
20. 20 in the baby set; 32 in the adult.
21. The skin.
22. Filtrum.
23. The larynx.
24. In the abdomen, behind the stomach.
25. Spanish influenza.

FAMILIAR POEMS QUIZ

1. *"Views from thy hand no worthy action done."* Author unknown.
2. "Rabbi Ben Ezra," by Robert Browning.
3. *"And what can be the use of him is more than I can see."* R. L. Stevenson's "My Shadow."
4. *"Sees God in clouds, or hears Him in the wind."* Pope's "Essay on Man."
5. James Whitcomb Riley.
6. *"Oh, London is a man's town, there's power in the air."*
7. *"It will not last the night; But ah, my foes, and Oh, my friends, It gives a lovely light."* Edna St. Vincent Millay.
8. "Thanksgiving Day," by Lydia Maria Child.
9. James Mason Knox, a great admirer of Kipling.
10. Lewis Carroll.
11. *"I'm sure we should all be as happy as kings."*
12. Dante Gabriel Rosetti.
13. "The Ancient Mariner," by Coleridge.
14. *"Than never to have loved at all."*
15. Keats.
16. Rubaiyat of Omar Khayyam.
17. *"Nor iron bars a cage."*
18. Arthur Hallam.
19. "The Vampire" by Rudyard Kipling.
20. *"Never the twain shall meet."*
21. Longfellow. The rest of the verse is *"Homekeeping hearts are happiest."*
22. Lowell.
23. *"One dead lamb is there."*
24. *"As You Like It."*
25. *"A-flying."*

FAMILIAR SONGS QUIZ

1. Al Smith.
2. "Show Boat."
3. "When You and I Were Young, Maggie."
4. Stephen C. Foster.
5. "My Old Kentucky Home."
6. "As Thousands Cheer."
7. Irving Berlin.
8. George Gershwin.
9. "School Days."
10. *"In a wooden shoe."*
11. *"A string of pearls to me."*
12. "Sweet Alice," of the song "Ben Bolt."
13. "Old Folks at Home," by Stephen Foster.
14. Mrs. Julia Ward Howe (1819–1910).
15. "America" and "God Save the King."
16. *"I was seeing Nellie Home."*
17. Negro spiritual.

18. *"Silver threads among the gold."*
19. "Madelon."
20. "Floradora."
21. "Over There."
22. *"And never brought to mind."*
23. The River Rye.
24. "Aloha Oe."
25. "Oh Promise Me."

Junior Quiz Number 1

1. Honey.
2. Ireland.
3. Salt water.
4. Three.
5. Robert Louis Stevenson.
6. Thermometer.
7. England, Scotland, Wales, Ireland, Isle of Man and Channel Islands.
8. Captain John Smith.
9. Before Christ and Anno Domini (in the year of Our Lord).
10. Scandinavia.
11. No, Sunday.
12. The silk worm.
13. Papoose is an Indian baby, porpoise is a fish.
14. Eight.
15. William Penn.
16. Pigeons.
17. George Herman (Babe) Ruth.
18. Italy.
19. A group of stars.

20. Congress.
21. Red.
22. Plural, the singular is datum.
23. Buffalo Bill.
24. The invention of the aeroplane.
25. Eastern, Central, Mountain, Pacific.

Junior Quiz Number 2

1. Balboa.
2. Empire State Building in New York City.
3. Rural free delivery.
4. Patrick Henry.
5. Bedloe's Island, New York Harbor.
6. John Philip Sousa.
7. Holland.
8. Apiary is a place where bees are kept; aviary, a large cage for birds.
9. Castor oil.
10. Stockholm, Rio de Janeiro, Canberra.
11. John Nance Garner.
12. Harpoon.
13. Oasis.
14. Rudyard Kipling.
15. West Indies.
16. Cygnet.
17. Hamelin, Germany.
18. Arizona and New Mexico.
19. A famous pirate.
20. Robin.
21. Peter.

22. Philadelphia.
23. Polaris or the Pole Star.
24. Soldier, scientist, composer, humorist.
25. Igloo.

BRAIN TEASER QUIZ

1. In the Plant Kingdom.
2. Appian Way.
3. Lawn-mower.
4. It is said to be miraculously balanced by a hair of Buddha.
5. "Gifts of the Magi," by O. Henry.
6. Because it is diffused more completely than light coming from a portion of the sky where direct sunlight exists.
7. "And these have smaller still to bite 'em; and so proceed ad infinitum."
8. Yes, absolute zero — 459° F. or — 273° C.
9. It is now generally accepted that they were written by Sir Philip Francis.
10. That of the Mongols under Kublai Khan.
11. The amethyst.
12. By marching his army around the walls and having them blow their ram's horns (trumpets).
13. Nanda Devi in the Himalayas, 25,645 feet. Its summit was reached August 29, 1936.
14. Lord Chancellor of England, in the House of Lords.
15. Over nine million have been taken from a single female.
16. Blue moon.
17. A frog has teeth, a toad has none.
18. 365.
19. Biskra.
20. Yes, by resonance.
21. No, not necessarily.
22. Water power.
23. Low pressure.
24. Tree sculpture, or the cutting of trees into grotesque shapes.
25. Jason.

SUPER QUIZ NUMBER 1

1. It is that part of the Arctic Ocean lying between Alaska and the Canadian Arctic Islands.
2. The lunar month.
3. Wolffia. It is about the size and shape of the head of a pin.
4. Prism-ornamented branching candlesticks.
5. William III of England was shorter than Mary, his consort, and therefore stood on a stool.
6. André Geraud, an influen-

tial newspaper man of Europe.

7. "The Burial of Sir John Moore," by Charles Wolfe.

8. Yes, the intersection of Colorado, New Mexico, Arizona and Utah.

9. Representative government, dual government, inalienable rights of the individual, independence of the judiciary, system of checks and balances, joint power of President and Senate in determination of foreign policy.

10. The inner ear or labyrinth.

11. Yes, the kiwi or apteryx of New Zealand.

12. More than 75 miles an hour.

13. Friction.

14. Xantippe.

15. The practice of marrying a brother's widow.

16. That part of a building rising above the roof which contains windows for lighting the interior.

17. "Non Sum Qualis Eram Bonae Sub Regno Cynarae," by Ernest Dowson.

18. "Death and Transfiguration," a Tone Poem by Richard Strauss.

19. Schizophrenia.

20. Rock on the Italian coast and whirlpool on the Sicilian coast.

21. Florence, Italy.

22. Senatus Populusque Romanus, the Senate and the Roman People.

23. It does not occupy a position in any constellation.

24. Approximately fifteen billion dollars.

25. John O'Groats.

Super Quiz Number 2

1. The human back, considered the most perfect curve.

2. Om mani pad me hum (O, the Jewel in the Lotus, Amen!).

3. Torii.

4. Circus Maximus and Coliseum.

5. Outer Mongolia.

6. According to Dr. Bakst of Columbia, 1 in about 1,000,-000,000.

7. Mah Jong.

8. Greyhound.

9. The Corbett-Fitzsimmons heavyweight championship bout.

10. Galvanism.

11. Tutuila, Samoa.

12. Arthur Krock of the New York Times.

13. Demosthenes.

14. Richard Wagner married Cosima Liszt.

15. Spider.

16. "All Gaul is divided into three parts."

17. Protactinium.
18. Scotland.
19. Arturo Toscanini.
20. Bacchus.
21. Goodbye. Literally, "Since it must be so" (Japanese).
22. Tennyson's "Higher Pantheism."
23. Chief Signal Officer at the time when the Weather Service was part of the Signal Corps.
24. In the crypt of the Cathedral in Granada, Spain.
25. Piece of mail incorrectly, insufficiently or indefinitely addressed.

Miscellaneous Quiz Number 1

1. Rome.
2. Oedipus.
3. Bank of England.
4. A mythical deity represented as a violent overbearing person. Now a violent, hot-tempered woman.
5. Geheime Staatspolizei— Secret State Police of Germany.
6. Thistle, Fleur-de-lys, lotus, pomegranate.
7. Thomas.
8. Mohammed.
9. Delhi, India.
10. United States.
11. Venice.

12. No.
13. In India, outcasts, members of the lowest classes whose touch is defilement to those of higher caste.
14. Caesar's.
15. William II of Germany and Nicholas II of Russia.
16. Southwest Europe, comprising Spain, Portugal, Catalonia.
17. The practice of having more than one husband.
18. Mississippi River.
19. Knowledge.
20. Hercules.
21. Keats' "Endymion."
22. As a war cry or gathering cry of the Scottish clans.
23. Separate strands of rope, splice.
24. Roger Bacon.
25. Wax works.

Miscellaneous Quiz Number 2

1. Both may be used.
2. No, they carry a wooden truncheon.
3. The loss of the steamship Titanic.
4. North, South and Stewart Islands.
5. Because of the supposed resemblance of the corona to the Crown of Thorns.
6. Deborah.

7. Letters written by Robert Louis Stevenson from his home in Samoa.
8. None, it is made of shellac and resin.
9. Simon Stylites.
10. Amateur Athletic Union.
11. No, there is no proof that such a person ever existed.
12. Strasbourg.
13. Yes, from seeds so small that it takes thirty thousand to weigh as much as a grain of wheat.
14. The nutria or coypu.
15. Lafayette.
16. Mediterranean and Red Seas.
17. Manufacture of soap.
18. Penguin.
19. Chinaware, originally made in Belleck, Ireland.
20. Legalized adoption of two metals for currency.
21. Dancing.
22. Aesop.
23. Helen of Troy.
24. 640.
25. Valparaiso, Chile.

MISCELLANEOUS QUIZ NUMBER 3

1. She sits.
2. Napoleon.
3. Senator Arthur H. Vandenberg of Michigan.

4. George Washington and James Madison.
5. Because he does miscellaneous jobs. Bus is an abbreviation of the Latin omnibus, meaning all.
6. The aorta.
7. Pulp of sugar cane after the juice has been extracted.
8. Attila.
9. Tea.
10. Its oracle.
11. Don Quixote's squire and servant.
12. Shanghai.
13. The leader.
14. A monument to the memory of one buried elsewhere.
15. None.
16. Lindbergh's plane, now in the Smithsonian Institution, Washington, D. C.
17. The Thursday after Trinity Sunday.
18. Violins.
19. Twenty-four.
20. Cardinal Newman.
21. Nadir.
22. A wine, produced in Italy.
23. Oxford, England.
24. Jaffa.
25. Walt Whitman.

MISCELLANEOUS QUIZ NUMBER 4

1. Vicuna.
2. Eleven.

3. Only one—Washington.
4. R. E. Olds.
5. Pith of a small tree growing in Formosa. There is no rice in it.
6. Jean de la Fontaine.
7. First baseman.
8. Hyacinth.
9. Sleeping sickness.
10. It is Greek and means many. As used today it means the common people or the crowd.
11. Hydrogen.
12. Nice, France.
13. Federal Deposit Insurance Corporation, Securities Exchange Commission, Federal Communications Commission.
14. Finland.
15. Cleopatra, in Shakespeare's "Antony and Cleopatra."
16. In the Middle Ages it was believed that saintly persons when dying gave off a sweet and delightful odor.
17. Auf Wiedersehen!
18. Ourselves alone.
19. An inn.
20. A successful rebellion is termed a revolution.
21. Mercury.
22. They will not achieve complete independence until the end of the ten-year transitional period in 1946.
23. The game of billiards.

24. A feast with nothing to eat.
25. "I Pagliacci."

MISCELLANEOUS QUIZ NUMBER 5

1. Coast of Antrim, Northern Ireland.
2. Georgius Rex, Latin for George, King.
3. Silver fox.
4. The Aletsch glacier.
5. It was Sheraton's favorite color.
6. French.
7. Death Valley Scotty.
8. The one who makes the call.
9. Cornelius Conway Felton, President of Harvard College, Louis Agassiz and Charles Sumner.
10. From Admiral Edward Vernon, nicknamed Old Grogram from the cloak he wore.
11. A kibitzer.
12. The Spartans.
13. Assassins of Presidents Garfield, McKinley and Lincoln.
14. Greenwich mean time.
15. Water.
16. Russia.
17. The moon, because it is so much closer to the earth.
18. Ulysses (Odysseus).
19. Fifteen years' service.
20. Somerset Maugham.
21. Famous English portrait and

historical painter. (1734–1802)

22. In the Salt River, Arizona.
23. June 25 and 26, 1876.
24. Sitting Bull.
25. Let it stand.

MISCELLANEOUS QUIZ NUMBER 6

1. Pittsburgh, National League vs. Boston, American League.
2. The Dead Sea.
3. "Equal Justice Under Law."
4. Four.
5. Shelley's "Ode to the West Wind."
6. Queen Victoria.
7. Buttercup.
8. Anatole France.
9. The United States Post Office Department.
10. Louisiana.
11. Thomas A. Edison.
12. Voluntary Aid Detachment.
13. Because there were five— Sandwich, Dover, Hythe, Romney and Hastings.
14. *Josephine Ford.*
15. Joseph Jefferson.
16. Geniuses, crises, stimuli.
17. Measuring a horse. A hand is 4 inches.
18. The Prime Minister of Great Britain.
19. It was originated in 1902 by Clifford Berryman, cartoonist of the Washington Star, after a bear hunt by President Theodore Roosevelt.
20. None. The story about Nero has no historical basis. The fiddle had not yet been invented.
21. William Jennings Bryan, July 10, 1896 in the Democratic Convention in Chicago.
22. In the Invalides in Paris.
23. Socrates.
24. Cantons.
25. San Francisco.

MISCELLANEOUS QUIZ NUMBER 7

1. The material at the head of the first column of the editorial page stating ownership, subscription and advertising rates.
2. James Monroe and Robert R. Livingston.
3. General Motors.
4. Yes, in so far as the Constitution is concerned. It makes no provision in regard to the sex of the President.
5. Telephones are now permitted but radios are not.
6. Stephen.
7. In the grounds of the Louisiana State Capitol.
8. No, 40 countries have adopted the idea.

9. The name given to the sack of Antwerp by Spanish troops in 1576.
10. About 22 per cent.
11. Hippocrates. The arrangement was subsequently used by Shakespeare.
12. Cedar.
13. For one pair of three thread hosiery, one hundred and thirty cocoons are required.
14. Will Rogers.
15. Under modern rules Cy Young in 1904 pitched the first perfect game—no runs, no hits and nobody reaching first base.
16. 150.
17. On the River Danube at the border of Hungary.
18. The *Santa Maria.*
19. Lake Mead.
20. Yes, the University of the State of New York is only an administrative Board of Regents.
21. Benjamin Franklin.
22. The English country home of Lady Astor, on the Upper Thames.
23. Adena Miller (Mrs. Kenneth F. Miller).
24. Nevada and California lead with one car to every 2.6 inhabitants.
25. They are the articles of faith of the Church of England, the acceptance of which is obligatory on its clergy.

MISCELLANEOUS QUIZ NUMBER 8

1. Intelligence quotient, a number denoting the intelligence of a person.
2. Congruent.
3. Delaware.
4. To rhyme with Sarah.
5. Italian.
6. Mountain in Macedonia believed by ancient Greeks to be the abode of their gods.
7. Benjamin.
8. London and Paris.
9. Shame to him who thinks evil of it. Motto of the Order of the Garter.
10. Vicksburg, Mississippi.
11. As long as 300 to 400 years.
12. A pen name or pseudonym.
13. Oxford and Cambridge.
14. 360.
15. From the town where it is produced, Cognac, France.
16. Junior organization of Camp Fire Girls.
17. Alexander the Great.
18. Fashions. It is a street in Paris where many famous dressmakers and milliners are located.
19. Mediterranean Sea near Sicily.
20. Shells of oysters and mussels.

21. Ante means before, anti means against or contrary to.
22. Editions of the classics by Aldus Manutius, Venetian printer.
23. Shakespeare's "Merchant of Venice."
24. Perch, pike.
25. One hundred.

MISCELLANEOUS QUIZ NUMBER 9

1. Cooperstown, New York.
2. It was first used officially in the text of the Irish Free State Treaty in 1921.
3. Any situation preferable to that occupied is a better 'ole. The allusion is to Captain Bairnsfather's soldier who refused to leave a shell hole until a better one was forthcoming.
4. Immortality, fecundity. When split by bursting seeds it symbolizes resurrection.
5. Dr. Douglas Hyde was 78 years old.
6. Bonds which correspond to United States Government bonds.
7. Yes, John Casimir, a Cardinal, was summoned to the throne of Poland in 1648.
8. In the code of this Athenian

law maker nearly every violation was a capital offense.
9. The House of Lords. The Lords in session are subject to none but the King.
10. Adolph Hitler.
11. Rene Descartes.
12. Moscow, Russia.
13. Major Whittlesey.
14. The Marion *Star*.
15. Louis Philippe, King of France (1830–48), because of his bourgeois manners and dress.
16. O. O. MacIntyre.
17. Jazz.
18. Unleavened bread eaten at Passover.
19. Torquemada.
20. The white.
21. Heinrich Heine.
22. Tremendous, stupendous, portendous, horrendous.
23. 5280.
24. The Library of Congress, Washington, D. C.
25. Midland, Lloyd's, Barclay, Westminster, National Provincial.

MISCELLANEOUS QUIZ NUMBER 10

1. Kentucky. They were Abraham Lincoln and Jefferson Davis.

2. According to law not oftener than once in 25 years.
3. *Queen Elizabeth.*
4. Sarah Bernhardt.
5. Yes.
6. Westminster Abbey.
7. Jawbone of an ass.
8. Lake Nemi, Italy.
9. One versed in the art of memory.
10. Japan.
11. Mona Lisa.
12. Center of the chin.
13. Dorothy Dix's column begun in 1896.
14. Stalagmites are formed on the floor of a cave, stalactites hang from the roof.
15. Argus. Juno put them in the tail of her peacock.
16. *Punch.*
17. Excalibur.
18. Pyrrhic victory.
19. Yes, Tibet.
20. New Hampshire.
21. Faneuil Hall, Boston, was rebuilt after its destruction by fire from the proceeds of lotteries.
22. Yes, a tied-to-cover stamp is worth more than the same stamp by itself.
23. Pride, covetousness, lust, anger, gluttony, envy, sloth.
24. *News of the World,* London.
25. Damascus in Syria and Toledo in Spain.

MISCELLANEOUS QUIZ
NUMBER 11

1. Ellen H. Underwood.
2. When it is not known whether she is married or single.
3. Rainfall.
4. André Citroën.
5. *Cyclops.*
6. Lucullus.
7. Phineas T. Barnum.
8. Turngain Arm, Cook Inlet, Alaska.
9. Charles II.
10. Roman Calendar. The ides of March would be the 15th, being the eight day after the nones.
11. 3140 miles.
12. Sir John Tenniel.
13. Floyd Gibbons.
14. Gold, frankincense and myrrh.
15. Vachel Lindsay.
16. Immigrant.
17. *Bellerophon.*
18. China.
19. Mayfair.
20. Jefferson City.
21. Andrew Jackson
22. Notre Dame.
23. Damp air.
24. Mona Lisa.
25. Switzerland.

MISCELLANEOUS QUIZ NUMBER 12

1. "The Women."
2. Museum of Pittsfield, Massachusetts.
3. Sir Walter Scott.
4. "Pagliacci."
5. President of the New York Stock Exchange.
6. Kentucky.
7. "Gone with the Wind."
8. Because of its extensive coal deposits.
9. Male sex.
10. Cramp in the muscles between the ribs.
11. College of William and Mary.
12. Annie Fellows Johnston.
13. The mother of King Tutankhamen.
14. Seismograph.
15. Oscar Wilde, Sir Walter Raleigh and Ralph Chaplin.
16. Ophir.
17. 69.57 yards.
18. It is from the Hebrew Mashiakh, meaning anointed one.
19. Judge Jeffreys. Universally condemned for his injustice and brutality, he was imprisoned and died in the Tower of London in 1689.
20. Noel Coward.
21. Richard Halliburton.
22. Dvorak's "New World Symphony."
23. The warm tropical seas, about 1800 miles north and south of the Equator.
24. The sun's gravity.
25. Fish.

MISCELLANEOUS QUIZ NUMBER 13

1. Jerusalem.
2. Saturn.
3. Danube.
4. Scotland.
5. Jean François Millet (1814–1875) a French artist who also painted "The Angelus."
6. Georgia. It is Stone Mountain.
7. Tunstall, Burslem, Hanley, Stoke, Longton.
8. Joaquin Miller (originally Cincinnatus Heine Miller), an American lawyer, editor, poet and playwright (1841–1913).
9. Yellowstone National Park (Geyser).
10. Oliver Cromwell's soldiers.
11. Balsa.
12. "Rembrandt's Mother," by Rembrandt.
13. George W. Russell.
14. East Hampton, Long Island.
15. French.
16. Naples.

17. Off the coast of Spain 130 miles south of Barcelona.
18. Napoleon's residence on the Island of Saint Helena.
19. Molten rock.
20. Gibraltar.
21. Meteors are luminous bodies familiarly called shooting stars. When they fall to the earth they are called meteorites.
22. The Pyramids.
23. Orography.
24. By knots per hour. A division on a ship's log line, marked by knots of rope, usually $\frac{1}{120}$ of a nautical mile apart. The number of knots paid out in 30 seconds ($\frac{1}{120}$ of an hour) is equivalent to the number of miles per hour at which the ship is moving. Hence the term knot has come to signify a nautical mile.
25. California.

MISCELLANEOUS QUIZ
NUMBER 14

1. Theodore Roosevelt. William Howard Taft.
2. Dewey, Hobson, Schley, Sampson, Roosevelt.
3. Republican leader in the McKinley era. He was U. S. Senator from Ohio in 1898.
4. Cavalry under Wood and Roosevelt in the Spanish-American War.
5. Simon Bolivar.
6. 231.
7. Vermont.
8. The last of the fighting Indian leaders. An Apache chief who died in 1909.
9. Queen, workers, drones.
10. Nathaniel Bacon.
11. A person who rushed into Indian Territory sooner than was legal.
12. McKinley.
13. Samuel Langhorne Clemens.
14. Franklin Pierce.
15. Illinois.
16. A parabola is a kind of curve; a parable is a story which teaches a moral.
17. Rudyard Kipling.
18. Quail and rail.
19. Twist.
20. Yellow jack is yellow fever; a yellow jacket is a wasp.
21. The man who stamped out yellow fever in Panama.
22. Rhinoceros is an animal; rhinitis is an inflammation of the inside of the nose.
23. (1) Steamboat; (2) cotton gin; (3) sewing machine; (4) reaper.
24. The temple of Athena, on the Acropolis; the most beautiful temple in Greece.
25. Samuel Adams.

MISCELLANEOUS QUIZ NUMBER 15

1. Benjamin Franklin, John Adams, John Jay.
2. To play dead.
3. Virginia.
4. Seventy square miles.
5. The opossum.
6. Connecticut.
7. Colorado.
8. William Jennings Bryan and Grover Cleveland.
9. Lincoln, Garfield, McKinley.
10. Lincoln's law office and Bryan's birth place.
11. (1) Henry George; (2) Edward Bellamy.
12. A protest march from Ohio to Washington, led by Jacob S. Coxey.
13. The artist who created the Gibson Girl.
14. A Cherokee Indian (1770–1842) who compiled an alphabet for the Cherokee tongue. The giant Sequoia trees are named in his honor.
15. (1) Edwin Markham; (2) Israel Zangwill.
16. Republican slogan in 1900.
17. Through the antennae.
18. The Grange.
19. The United States average is over 4,000 pounds.
20. Iowa.
21. Hydrochloric acid; water; salt.
22. An extinct volcano, the highest peak in the Andes of South America. Elevation 23,097 feet.
23. The hill forming the center of Athens.
24. (a) Netherlands; (b) France, (c) Haiti.
25. Dr. Mary Walker, an American physician and dress reformer (1832–1919). At the age of 29 she discarded female attire.

MISCELLANEOUS QUIZ NUMBER 16

1. Ro-day'-o
2. *Success.*
3. Edward Payson Weston.
4. Lethal gas.
5. Sir Henry Raeburn (1756–1823). A Scottish portrait painter.
6. Muskrat and skunk.
7. Dice.
8. Gustavus Adolphus of Sweden (1594–1632).
9. Chestnut.
10. Raised type for the blind.
11. Robert Louis Stevenson.
12. Chinese ships.
13. Japanese cherry.
14. Buffalo Bill (William Frederick Cody).

15. The rotation of the earth on its axis.
16. Chopsticks.
17. Chinese, meaning prince, but often used to denote powerful industrial magnate.
18. A silversmith.
19. Revival of Learning.
20. Old-fashioned photographs. The name comes from Louis Daguerre, inventor of one process of photography.
21. Golf.
22. January 1, 1901.
23. Moscow, U.S.S.R.
24. 2240.
25. Bertha Krupp, for whom the Big Bertha was named.

MISCELLANEOUS QUIZ NUMBER 17

1. An island off the coast of Venezuela, in the Netherlands West Indies.
2. She was raised, reconditioned and sold to Venezuela by Secretary of State Philander Knox.
3. Dictator of Venezuela from 1909 to 1935, the most ruthless, cruel and perhaps brilliant dictator that the modern world has known.
4. Benjamin Franklin.
5. East St. Louis, Illinois.
6. A brilliant French novelist, author of "I Accuse."

7. "Portrait of My Mother."
8. The Pyramids, the Hanging Gardens of Babylon, the Tomb of Mausolus, the Temple of Diana at Ephesus, the Colossus of Rhodes, the Statue of Jupiter by Phidias, and the Pharos (Lighthouse) of Alexandria.
9. The 21st verse of the 7th Chapter of Ezra.
10. Dominion of Canada.
11. A hall erected on University Heights, New York, in 1900 for use as a memorial of great Americans.
12. A synonym for no choice at all. It is derived from a liveryman named Hobson, who forced his customers to take whichever horse happened to be nearest to the stable door, or none at all.
13. General Zachary Taylor, so called by his soldiers during the Mexican War.
14. For his American dictionary.
15. Hansel und Gretel.
16. The piano.
17. Sun-dried bricks made of clay.
18. A bell tower.
19. A gem upon which a figure or an ornament is cut in relief.
20. Mt. Whitney, California, 14,501 feet. Mt. McKinley,

in Alaska, is 20,300 feet high.

21. Saccharin.
22. The thyroid gland.
23. Words pronounced the same but differing in spelling and in meaning.
24. Hiram.
25. "Proclaim liberty throughout all the land unto all the inhabitants thereof"—taken from the Bible, Lev. 25:10.

MISCELLANEOUS QUIZ NUMBER 18

1. San Marino, located in central Italy. It contains 32 square miles.
2. Alfred Lunt and Lynn Fontanne.
3. (1) Dale Carnegie; (2) Irving D. Tressler.
4. Yehudi Menuhin.
5. Governor A. B. Chandler of Kentucky.
6. Senator Norris of Nebraska.
7. John D. Rockefeller, Jr.
8. The lips.
9. Ecuador, Peru and Columbia.
10. Byron.
11. A woman's skirt stiffened with a horse hair fabric or wire hoops.
12. Tea.
13. Sheep.

14. Solicitor General of the United States.
15. Copper.
16. The warp.
17. Rhapsody.
18. Shellac.
19. Those descended from the popular Latin tongue. Spanish, French, Italian, Portuguese.
20. Yankee Stadium, New York.
21. It means Member of Parliament.
22. " 'Tis folly to be wise."
23. Because Spain has no castles.
24. Day of Atonement, a Jewish holiday.
25. The pointed arch.

MISCELLANEOUS QUIZ NUMBER 19

1. By friction of the rough basal part of its fore wings.
2. For the novel that best typifies some phase of American life.
3. Witwatersrand area in South Africa.
4. The cup which the Savior blessed and passed to His disciples at the Last Supper.
5. All lighthouses are painted white, or white with black stripes.
6. London.
7. Because it was made almost entirely of glass.

8. Ogpu.
9. The gospel for the day contains the story of the Miraculous Feeding of the Five Thousand.
10. The raccoon.
11. Because a portion of the forbidden fruit is supposed to have stuck in Adam's throat.
12. The entire name must be exactly the same.
13. According to custom, for the first year following her marriage.
14. It is a whirlpool off the Norwegian coast.
15. Rudyard Kipling.
16. No, the name is given to the ulnar nerve at the back of the elbow.
17. A flat-bottomed row boat used by fishermen. A light open four-wheeled Russian carriage.
18. Citroën automobiles.
19. Poe's "Murders in the Rue Morgue."
20. During the World War (1918).
21. Saint Walston, whose feast day is May 30.
22. More than two.
23. The eel.
24. Passes or free theatre tickets, so-called from the famous shot, Annie Oakley, because they are usually perforated, as by bullet holes.
25. Kerosene lamp.

MISCELLANEOUS QUIZ NUMBER 20

1. Misogynist.
2. Percy Bysshe Shelley.
3. A redan is part of a defense works with a salient angle in front. A sedan is an enclosed passenger vehicle.
4. 122 feet per second.
5. An orchid.
6. Abraham Lincoln.
7. Grover Cleveland.
8. Diogenes, the Greek cynic philosopher.
9. Phil Spitalny.
10. Finland.
11. Paul Redfern.
12. An Episcopal clergyman who published a highly imaginary biography of George Washington in 1800.
13. Robert Burns.
14. Castor and Pollux.
15. Eight and one-third pounds.
16. Journalist. Publisher of the New York *World*.
17. California.
18. A grass.
19. Leningrad, Russia.
20. Walter Winchell.
21. Thigh bones or femurs.
22. About 12 miles.
23. As it should be; proper.

24. Baseball term for a screw-ball.
25. The late Edgar W. Howe, Kansas editor and publisher was so called.

MISCELLANEOUS QUIZ NUMBER 21

1. Edward the Black Prince was so ill that he was carried in a litter to lead his army against Limoges.
2. The late Will Rogers.
3. United States.
4. Cape Flattery, Washington, and a point on the Florida coast south of Miami, 2,835 miles.
5. In Japanese, exalted gate.
6. The name of the Marquis of Martinet.
7. Boake Carter.
8. The boundary between Pennsylvania and Maryland comprising the parallel of latitude 39° 43′ 2.3″, as set by the surveyors Charles Mason and Jeremiah Dixon in 1767.
9. Henry Ford's Peace Ship Expedition.
10. Michelangelo.
11. Robert Harper, who in 1747 established a ferry there.
12. "Shooting of Dan McGrew," by Robert W. Service.

13. Drone.
14. Latin.
15. Florence Nightingale, the famous English nurse.
16. Charles II, Sirloin.
17. London Times.
18. Tower of London.
19. Proxima Centauri.
20. Chinaware.
21. From the Latin plagiarus, a kidnaper, stealer, abductor of a slave or child.
22. Italian.
23. Grand Army of the Republic.
24. Louisiana.
25. Zoetrope, kinematoscope, phasmotrope.

MISCELLANEOUS QUIZ NUMBER 22

1. The banyan.
2. In English newspapers the personal column is known as the agony column.
3. This cold Siberian seaport is as far south as the French Riviera.
4. Air in motion.
5. Any carpet woven on a broad loom.
6. They were extensively exported to Turkey to be used as turbans.
7. A Spanish dance.
8. Yes, because of the presence of millions of tiny red plants.

9. There is none. The same answer goes for chimney.
10. The voice of Stentor.
11. No, hairs are glued in to enhance the appearance of certain furs.
12. Mizpah. "The Lord watch between me and thee when we are absent one from another."
13. Caspian Sea.
14. The purse hanging from a Scotch Highlander's belt.
15. Henry Hudson, the explorer.
16. Along the western coastline.
17. Domrémy, France.
18. Chauvinism, from Nicolas Chauvin, one of Napoleon's soldiers, who even after the Emperor's fall, continued to demonstrate such patriotism that he won the ridicule of his comrades.
19. Island of Trinidad; Sir Walter Raleigh.
20. Both are right, only they are two different men.
21. Shoddy.
22. No, some of the larger countries with no legal standard time are China, Mongolia, Tibet, Persia, Arabia.
23. Texas.
24. East Texas.
25. Sandwich, ampere, nicotine, volt, guillotine, boycott, watt, Fletcherism, wisteria, mackintosh, Machiavellian, davenport, galvanize, mesmerize, mercerize, sanforize, Zeppelin.

MISCELLANEOUS QUIZ NUMBER 23

1. 2,020,000,000.
2. Shakespeare's "Merchant of Venice."
3. After Solon, the Athenian law-giver, who was entrusted with revising the Athenian constitution.
4. Nine hundred and sixty.
5. Putting money into productive employment so that through salaries gained by wage earners, production will be stimulated.
6. No, length is always the greater dimension.
7. Mount Kilimanjaro, 19,320 feet.
8. Yes.
9. General Election Day.
10. Opossum.
11. String, wind and percussion.
12. "When he is old he will not depart from it."
13. "The Jazz Singer."
14. Milton Cross.
15. Funchal, Madeira, where he died in exile.
16. Cardinal Wolsey.
17. Sir Isaac Newton.
18. George Frederick Handel.

19. Humpty Dumpty in "Through the Looking Glass."
20. David Sarnoff.
21. First Families of Virginia.
22. Button Gwinnett.
23. Samuel Taylor Coleridge.

The poem was "Kubla Khan."
24. Seven dollars.
25. (1) Educator; (2) Member of Congress; (3) designer; (4) 1938 Pulitzer poetry prize winner; (5) Minister to Norway; (6) radio artist.